METALWORKING MADE EASY

WILLIAM J. BECKER
Instructor of Industrial Arts
Boynton Junior High School, Ithaca, N. Y.

THE BRUCE PUBLISHING COMPANY
MILWAUKEE

PREFACE

The projects in this book are primarily intended for the introductory metal shop. They have been used successfully in junior high school work. While it is expected that individual shops will vary the application of the material, it has been discovered that the best construction has resulted when the directions given were followed. They have been written so that any boy of a satisfactory junior high school level should have no difficulty in following them. In many cases considerable latitude has been allowed to permit individual design and this phase of the work should be encouraged.

This book was written over a period of five years for the students in the author's shop. Each job has been tried and accepted by them. Whenever an error was discovered by either the instructor or a student, it was immediately corrected. Many projects were eliminated because they did not prove satisfactory.

Since all of the projects require the use of common tools, the operations used in many of the objects will satisfy the requirements of various courses of study. Shops do vary, however, in equipment and this will necessitate some changes in the manner of construction.

The jobs are divided into three main divisions — art metal, sheet metal, and ornamental iron — and are arranged in the order of difficulty. They are offered to aid the student and teacher in the selection of jobs and not as an ironclad course of study.

The author wishes to thank the following teachers and student teachers for the suggestions which they offered: Louis W. Ulrich, V. T. Caruana, Albert-Nardiello, Theodore Gode, John Avery, R. D. Elton, Arthur Decker, and James W. Hatch.

WILLIAM J. BECKER

Ithaca, N. Y.
March, 1942

CONTENTS

SECTION I
SHEET-METAL PROJECTS

SECTION II
ART-METAL PROJECTS

SECTION III
ORNAMENTAL IRON PROJECTS

INTRODUCTION

Ability and skill in following written directions, whether it be a blue-print, the instructions accompanying a new machine, a kitchen recipe, or a road map, should be developed as a part of every student's education. The projects offered in this book were written in job-sheet form in order to help develop this ability. They have been selected because of their simplicity and are particularly recommended for beginners in metal shop. For this reason it is suggested that the directions be followed step by step. As progress is made in the ability to follow directions, improvement in performing operations and finishing jobs will be apparent. By this time, individual ideas will probably be offered. This should be encouraged by the instructor who should use various methods to promote the students' growth in work and design.

Devices that will enlarge or change ideas in this or other books go far toward the ultimate goal of every shop instructor, that is, the development of original ideas and jobs on the part of the students.

Equipment and Tools. The list of equipment and tools below will serve as a partial guide for the construction of the jobs in this book. It is not claimed that this list is complete, but the tools mentioned are necessary to complete the jobs, and at the same time will serve as a guide in equipping a shop. Undoubtedly many instructors will substitute other tools when different methods are used to do the work.

Certain processes can be simplified through the use of jigs. These have not been listed because it is felt that the instructor will use, improvise, and build these when the need arises.

No. 4 hand groover.
Hand seamer.
Set of solid punches.
Set of rivet sets.
¾-in. hollow punch.
Tin snips, regular.
Hawkbill snips.
Hack saw.
Bending jig for wrought iron.
Set of cold chisels.
Calipers, outside.
Scales, 12 in.
Circumference rule.
Scribers or scratch awls.
Dividers.

Safety goggles.
Drill press.
Drilling vise.
Shop benches.
Bench anvil.
Machinists' vises.
Sheet-metal stakes — square, blow-horn, and beakhorn.
Bar folder.
Squaring shears.
Universal machine — turning, burring, etc.
Slip form roller.
Grinder.
Spot welder.

Soldering furnace.
Buffer.
Power hack saw.
Hand drill.
Set of number jobbers twist drills.
Set of fractional jobbers twist drills.
Screw driver — 4-6 in.
Soldering copper — app. 1 lb. per pair.
Prick or center punch.
Pliers — side cutters, needle nose, machinists'.
Assortment of files.
Combination square.
Hand vise.
Etching equipment — acid jar, small brushes, etc.
Assortment of small C clamps.
Set of machine-screw taps and dies.
Set of machine-bolt taps and dies.
⅛-in. NPT die and tap.
Painting equipment.
No. 4 raising hammer for sheet metal.

Machinists' hammer — app. 12 oz.
Setting hammer.
Large-size hammer — app. 2-lb. ball peen.
Maple or iron form for raising 4-in. tray.
Various design punches such as matting tools and Navajo design.
Various mallets — wood, rawhide, leather faced.
Set of small jewelers' files.
Jewelers' saw and jig.
Various art-metal planishing hammers.
Raising hammer.
Chasing hammer.
Chasers, straight.
Tongs for round work.
Tongs for square work.
Stillson wrench — small.
Crescent wrench — small.
Monkey wrench — medium, for twisting wrought iron.

Materials Required. Each project has a list of the important materials required. As far as possible, the materials that have been listed will be found in most metal shops. In most cases it will be possible to substitute metals of a similar nature for the ones suggested. Most of the jobs are small enough so that the shop faced with a limited supply of material can use such items as tin cans and scrap copper. The tin-can stock can be adapted to the sheet-metal projects.

No attempt has been made to list bolts, nails, rivets, screws, solder, and the finishing materials required in the construction of the job. These smaller but necessary supplies are mentioned in the directions.

Supplies. This is a complete list of the stock used in the projects, exclusive of small fastenings, wire, solder, and so on.

IX tin plate either coke or charcoal finish.
Galvanized sheet iron, 26 ga.
Black sheet iron, 18, 22, and 26 ga.
Sheet copper, either cold or hot rolled, 14, 18, and 22 ga.
Sheet brass, either half hard or soft, 18 and 22 ga.
Sheet German silver (nickel silver or garalloy), 18 ga.
Sheet aluminum, 18 ga.
Tinned iron wire, No. 5 and 13.
Flat cold-rolled wire, round edge, 1/16 by ¼ in.
Cold-rolled steel, 3/16 in. round.

Wrought iron (soft mild steel).

1/16 by ⅜ in.		⅛ by ¾ in.	
1/16 by ½ in.		3/16 by ¾ in.	
⅛ by ½ in.		⅜ by ⅜ in.	
⅛ by ⅝ in.			

In addition, soldering supplies, steel wool, rivets, nuts and machine screws, emery cloth, buffing supplies, etching material, hack-saw blades, jewelers' saw blades, rags, painting supplies, drawing equipment, carbon paper, and squared paper are also required.

Layouts and Designs. The type of drawing used in this book to show the construction of jobs is varied according to the point each is trying to illustrate. If a mechanical drawing would best illustrate a point and a pictorial drawing another, each was used in its place.

In regard to student sketching and planning, it is advisable for school shops to relate some form of drawing to the shopwork. Many might feel that since the drawings in this and other books are quite complete that this phase can be overlooked. Nothing is farther from the truth because planning is an important phase of any work. Instructors can relate their shop drawing program to this book in various ways. Working drawings can be required before building each job, and after it has been completed the students can be encouraged to submit original ideas. Especially in the art-metal section is original work to be encouraged, and everyone can contribute something to it. The sketches in this book give a number of designs, but under the directions the students are encouraged to submit their own ideas. The shop instructor should certainly assist and persuade his pupils to exert originality.

The use of squared or graph paper will make easy the preparation of art-metal sketches. If the student will enlarge the reduced working drawings, it will provide good experience prior to the preparation of original sketches.

In many cases, instructors will deem it advisable to prepare patterns or jigs for the construction of some of the jobs. The layout type of drawing is readily adaptable to pattern preparation. The shop teacher may find that a student who has made a working drawing will find it much easier to interpret job drawings or blueprints made by the instructor.

Many times it has been found helpful to have certain prepared teaching aids for the students' appreciation of design and drawing. Wall charts showing types of forged wrought-iron ends, finishes, scale measurement, effects possible on art-metal bracelets, and so forth, will be helpful to student planning.

Materials Required. It will be noticed that all of the projects start by having the student fill out a bill of material. While many shops may not require this procedure, the use of such a form is increasing. Besides showing the students the need of an accurate list of supplies, the instructor will have an accurate record of everything constructed or being constructed in the shop, an inventory of supplies in stock, and also may use it as a system for grading. In those places where the student must pay for the material it can be used as a record or receipt of payment. The simple form shown has proved advantageous and the instructor will undoubtedly find additional uses for it.

Name ....

Period ....

Project ....

List of Materials   Price
 1 ....
 2 ....
 3 ....
 4 ....
 5 ....
 6 ....
 7 ....
 8 ....
 9 ....
10 ....
11 ....
12 ....
13 ....
14 ....
15 ....

Mark ....

To aid the student in figuring costs, it might be well to prepare price sheets listing the cost of the main materials supplied in the school shop. These sheets can be inserted into celluloid folders so that they will not be smudged. Another system is to allow the students to get the prices directly from company price catalogues.

Questions. Since industrial arts relates to the study of industry, the *why* phase of construction and other related matter is considered important. At the end of each job appear five questions which are intended to help the student master some of the fundamentals of metalwork. These questions may be used in any manner that the instructor sees fit. Some might urge the students to write out the answers after completing a job, others might allow groups or the class to exchange ideas on these questions, while others might augment the questions with some of their own. It is expected that the method of use will vary, and, after all, the important point is to get the students to realize that industrial arts is more than completing a series of jobs.

To assist the student, and the instructor as well, references are given at the end of each question indicating where the answer may be found.

Finishing Products. An important feature of any job is the application of the finish. To allow latitude for the pupil and the instructor, most of the finishing is left to their discretion. Kinds of finishes and their application vary in each shop and individual. In fact, variations, within control, should be encouraged in order to avoid stereotyped shop procedure. Some of the instructions recommend a finish, but in most cases the piece may be finished as desired.

For the purpose of guiding those who desire it, the following list of finishes is given. Methods of applying them will be found in the various books on metalworking which are listed in the bibliography.

Art metal
    Polished and lacquered.
    Satin finish either with acid or wire buff.
    Crystal finish with acid.
    Liver of sulphur for effects on copper.
    Ammonium sulphide for a fuming colored effect on copper.
    Butter of antimony for an oxidized effect on brass.
    Antique effects of chemicals on copper and brass.
    Coloring through heating.

Sheet metal and ornamental iron
    Cleaned, polished, and then waxed or lacquered.
    Flat black enamel.
    Four-hour enamels or lacquers.
    Four-hour enamels blown with bronzing powder.
    Antiqued with a combination of enamels.
    Burned finish with an oil rub.
    Crystal or crackle finish.

Safety. A most important consideration in the teaching of any school subject is safety. This is especially true in the shop. We are all aware of the tremendous accident toll of present-day living and in the increasing attention being paid to safety programs. Schools are being called upon more and more to aid in combating this scourge of modern times. In this book the attention of the student is drawn to specific dangers when they arise. Some of the questions at the end of the jobs endeavor to drive safety hints across to the student. But in the main the instructor should and will be the most important influence. Such items as proper guards on machines, proper machines and tools, proper working methods on the part of the teacher and pupil, correct shop conduct and attitudes, good lighting, good safety posters, and other visual aids will help more than the safety taught in this book.

How to Use This Book. Based on the assumption that this book is for the beginner, it would be wise for the instructor to allow the student some choice of project in the section being worked. For instance, if the student is working on the art-metal projects, he should be allowed to choose one from this group providing it is included in the operations considered necessary by either the instructor or course of study. A posted sheet giving the selection of projects would be valuable to the shop.

It is advisable before starting to work for the student to read the lesson in its entirety in order to get a general idea of the construction. Then, depending on the shop organization, the preparation of a working drawing would be in order. This might vary from a very simple sketch under certain circumstances to a mechanical drawing under others. Certain projects require the preparation of original designs or patterns, and this should be done now. The bill of materials should be prepared as indicated. As mentioned before, the student should list the cost of materials. Just before starting the job it might be best for the instructor to approve the drawing and the bill of material.

In most shops some system exists whereby the student checks his stock before cutting it. This can be done through a student stock clerk or the instructor himself.

While the student is performing various operations the instructor can help in various ways. Class demonstrations or unit working exhibit of basic tool operations or even a complete or partial construction of a particular article are advisable. For a class just starting metalwork, the construction of an entire job for their benefit will arouse considerable interest. Individual aid is valuable and often necessary.

After the job has been completed, the workmanship should be graded. This can be done by the pupil and rechecked by the instructor. At the same time, the student can indicate the completion of operations on the progress chart used in the shop. Finally, the questions should be answered.

SECTION I

SHEET-METAL PROJECTS

MONOGRAM BOOK ENDS

This monogrammed book end, made from a single piece of black sheet iron, can be used to hold small books on either a desk or table. If you desire, you may finish each of the book ends with Morocco crackle enamel.

MATERIALS REQUIRED

2 pieces, 22-ga. black sheet iron, 7½ by 4 in.

DIRECTIONS

1. Make out a bill of materials and have the instructor approve it.

2. Cut out the stock as listed on the bill of materials.

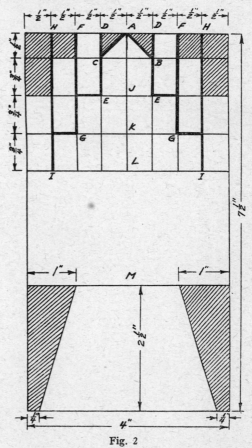

Fig. 1

3. Using emery cloth, remove the loose black scale from both pieces.

4. Lay out both pieces as shown in Figure 2.

5. After checking with the shop model, cut only these lines in the following order: *DE, FG,* and *HI.*

6. Cut away all the shaded sections shown in Figure 2.

7. Place the book ends on the bench, with the layout lines facing up. Center a ½-in. iron bar on line *J.* Now bend the outside loops around the bar either by hand or with the aid of a pliers. (See the instructor for a demonstration.)

8. Perform the same operation along lines *K* and *L.*

9. Using a file, remove any sharp edges.

10. Place the piece in a sheet-metal vise, and bend on line *M* so that the base will be at a right angle to the sides (Fig. 3).

Fig. 2

11. After checking the color harmony with the instructor, paint as desired.

12. While the paint is drying, decide on the monogram you want, and then lay it out on squared paper.

13. With the aid of carbon paper, transfer the design to the cardboard.

14. Cut it out with a razor blade.

15. Place the template on the book end, and hold it in place with paper clips.

16. Fill in the design with light colored enamel. (Check with the instructor.)

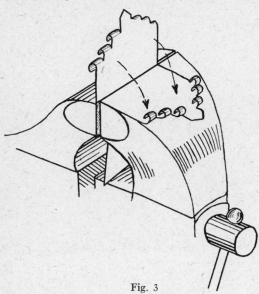

Fig. 3

REFERENCES

A. *Essentials of Metalworking*, Berg and Wing (Manual Arts Press).

B. *Metalwork Essentials*, Tustison and Kranzusch (Bruce Publishing Co.).

C. *Sheet Metal Work*, Trew and Bird (Manual Arts Press).

QUESTIONS

1. What is galvanized sheet iron? Tell how it is manufactured (Ref. C, p. 6).

2. Read Unit 7 of Reference B, which deals with the bending of sheet metals. Then explain how you bent the base of the book end at right angles to the sides.

3. Tell why and where you use right- and left-hand snips.

4. Explain why it is necessary to file the edges of a piece of sheet metal after you have cut it with a snips.

5. What is meant by an opaque finish? (Ref. B, p. 103.)

"DUCKY" NAPKIN RING

Being rather "tricky" in design, this napkin ring ought to persuade our younger brothers and sisters to fold their napkins. If you wish to enamel the finished job, make the ring from black iron and weld the joints. On the other hand, if you desire to have a shiny appearance, make it from tin plate and solder the joints.

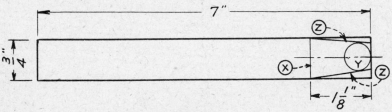

MATERIALS REQUIRED

IX tin plate (for soldered job); or 26-ga. black iron (for welded job).

Ring — 1 piece, ¾ by 7 in.

Tail — 2 pieces, ⅞ by 1¼ in.

Feet — 2 pieces, ¼ by 1¼ in.

Fig. 5

DIRECTIONS

1. Make out the bill of materials and have the instructor approve it.

2. Cut out the stock as listed in the bill of materials.

Ring

3. Lay out the ring as shown in Figure 6. Draw the lines in the following order: line X, followed by a ½-in. circle, Y; then the diagonal lines Z.

Fig. 6

4. Cut out along the diagonal lines and the circle at the end (Fig. 6).

5. If the job is to be made of black iron, use emery cloth to remove the black oxide where the weld is to be made.

6. Form the job round, as shown in Figure 5. Do this until you have a 1½-in. circle. NOTE: The piece will overlap while it is being formed in the form roller.

7. Solder or weld the square end in place as required.

8. Using the correct stake and mallet, bend the neck and head of the duck in place.

Tail

9. Lay out and cut the tailpiece, as shown in Figure 7.

10. Curve it slightly on the stake and solder it in place. If welded, clean both pieces of iron in the places to be welded.

11. Curve the legpieces slightly and then solder or weld them in place.

12. If the ring is made of tin plate, polish it with steel wool; if made of black iron, clean it with emery cloth and give it a coat of enamel.

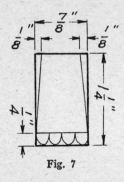

Fig. 7

REFERENCES
A. *Metal Work*, Jones (Bruce Publishing Co.).

B. *School and Home Shopwork*, Schultz and Schultz (Allyn and Bacon).

QUESTIONS
1. Before spot welding, why is the black oxide removed from black sheet iron?

2. How long should a piece of tin plate be cut to make a simple napkin ring 1¾ in. in diameter? (Ref. A, pp. 12, 13.)

3. Describe briefly how tin plate is made (Ref. B, p. 192).

4. What are the three main methods of drawing the outline or shape to which sheet metal is to be cut for a job? (Ref. B, pp. 193–194.)

5. Why are soldering coppers made from copper? (Ref. A, p. 66.)

FLAT PAN

This pan may be used for numerous purposes. It will serve as a storage box for nails, postage stamps, marbles, and many other things. If you would like to make it different from the size given under the directions, follow the instructions just below this paragraph. Possibly partitions, dividing the box

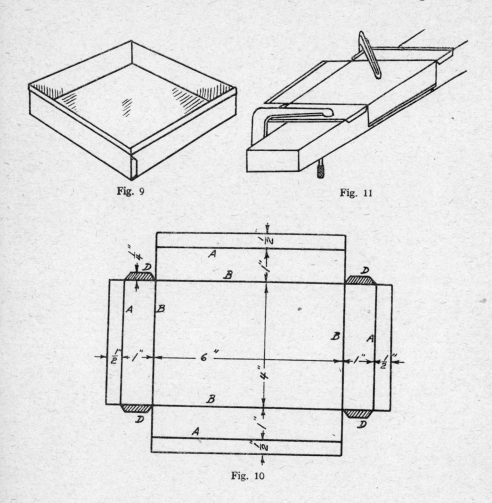

Fig. 9

Fig. 11

Fig. 10

into sections, would make it more valuable for your needs; your instructor will show you how to do this.

If you wish to make the box a different size from that given in the directions, use the following method:

1. Determine the height, length, and width that you want the box to be.

2. Multiply the height by two, and add 1 in.

3. To get the length of the material required, add the result from Instruction No. 2 to the length of your box (determined in Instruction No. 1).

4. To get the width of the metal required, add the result from Instruction No. 2 to the width of your box (determined in No. 1 above).

MATERIALS REQUIRED

IX tin plate — 1 piece, 7 by 9 in.

DIRECTIONS

1. Make out a bill of material and have the instructor approve it.

2. Cut the material to 7 by 9 in.

3. Lay out the metal as shown in Figure 10, drawing the lines in the following order: *A, B,* and flaps *D;* there are four of each.

4. Check your layout with the instructor, and then cut it out as shown in Figure 10.

5. With the bar folder, turn a double 3/16-in. hem on all four sides, along lines *A.*

6. Clamp the form to a stake (Fig. 11) and bend the box to shape with the hems on the outside. Bend the long sides first, including the flaps (Fig. 9). Bend the sides on a square stake.

7. Solder the flaps in place on the outside. Make sure that they fit tightly against the sides, so that the solder will not run into the inside.

8. Wash off the surplus flux, wipe it dry, and clean with fine steel wool.

REFERENCES

A. *A Course in Sheet Metal Work,* Bollinger (Bruce Publishing Co.).

B. *General Metal Work,* Grayshon (D. Van Nostrand).

C. *Metal Work,* Jones (Bruce Publishing Co.).

D. *School and Home Shopwork,* Schultz and Schultz (Allyn and Bacon).

QUESTIONS

1. If you desire a box 7 by 4 by 1 in., from what size material would you cut it? (See the instructions at the beginning of the lesson; and also Ref. A above.)

2. List eight methods of fastening iron parts (Ref. A, p. 35).

3. "Mechanical drawing is a universal language." Explain the meaning of this statement (Ref. D, p. 7).

4. Give the names of four fluxes (Ref. C, p. 68).

5. What is the meaning of the phrase "nonferrous" metals? (Ref. C, p. 54.)

MEMORANDUM HOLDER

This paper holder will help you keep a supply of memorandum paper at hand. An ordinary roll of adding-machine tape is used instead of sheets which are easily blown away.

MATERIALS REQUIRED

IX tin plate.

Body—1 piece, 7¾ by 7¾ in.

Bottom — 1 piece, 4¼ by 7½ in.

Bails—2 pieces, ¼ by 4½ in.

Front roller — 1 piece, ½ by 3⅝-in. dowel

Paper shaft — 1 piece, ⅜ by 3⅝-in. dowel

NOTE: If the shop has a spot welder, substitute black iron for the tin plate and weld the job wherever soldering is called for.

Fig. 13

DIRECTIONS

1. Make out a bill of material and have the instructor approve it.

2. Cut out the materials as listed above.

Body

3. Lay out the pattern shown in Figure 14 together with the hole positions.

4. Transfer the pattern or layout to the metal.

5. Use a center punch before drilling the 1/16-in. holes.

6. Remove the excess material in the following order: with a squaring shears make the cut marked 1; and then with a hand snips make the cuts marked 2, 3, 4, and 5.

7. Smooth the rough edges with a file.

8. Bend seam X in Figure 14 with a mallet and a square stake or else on a hand seamer. Flatten the seam with a mallet.

9. Make the bends A and B in Figure 15. Clamp the metal to the stake so that the bend will be in the same direction as the seam.

10. Bend the paper guide up with the fingers.

Bottom

11. With a bar folder, make right-angle bends along both long edges, ¼ in. wide.

Paper Bails

12. Make a right-angle bend ⅜ in. from the end of the paper bails (A, Fig. 16).

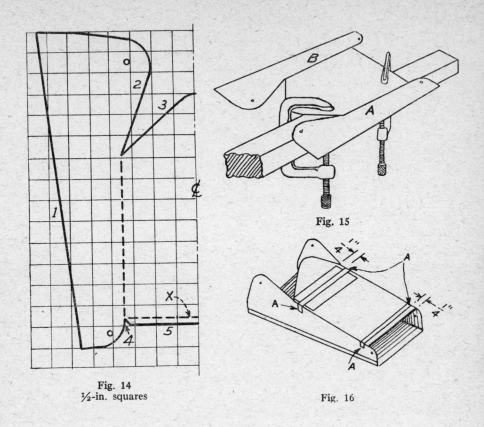

Fig. 14
½-in. squares

Fig. 15

Fig. 16

Front Roller and Paper Shaft

13. Check to see that the ends are square. Sandpaper them and punch a hole in the center of each with a scratch awl to serve as a guide for drilling.

14. With a hand drill, make a 1/16-in. hole ½ in. deep.

Assembly

15. Solder the bottom in place.

16. Solder the paper bails ¼ in. from each end, keeping a piece of thin sheet metal in place (Fig. 16). This will hold the bails high enough to pass the paper.

17. Put the front roller in place and drive an escutcheon into each end. Be sure that the roller turns freely.

18. Paint the holder, if desired. Do not paint the top of the body or the paper shaft, because it will interfere with the operation of the roller and prevent the roller from sliding readily.

19. Slip the roll of paper over the shaft and use the escutcheon pin to fasten it in place.

REFERENCES

A. *General Metal Work*, Grayshon (D. Van Nostrand).

B. *Sheet Metal Workers Manual*, Broemel (Frederick J. Drake).

C. *Metal Work*, Jones (Bruce Publishing Co.).

QUESTIONS

1. What is black sheet iron? What are some of the processes in its manufacture? (Ref. A, p. 3.)

2. How is spot welding accomplished? (Ref. B, p. 361.)

3. Is it impractical to weld thick metal with a spot welder? Why? (Ref. B, p. 362.)

4. Make a list giving ten products made from sheet metal (Ref. B, p. 11).

5. Name three ways of finishing sheet metal (Ref. C, p. 104).

WHISTLE

A whistle — most any boy or girl can use one. Whether it is used for refereeing a game or in connection with scout work, its blast will be quite adequate. By substituting a round cork instead of a pea, additional noise can be obtained.

MATERIALS REQUIRED

IX tin plate.
Disks — 2 pieces, 1¼ by 1¼ in.
Circle — 1 piece, 1 by 3¾ in.
Mouthpiece — 1 piece, ⅝ by 1¾ in.
Handle — 1 piece, 1¼ by 3½ in.

DIRECTIONS

1. Make out a bill of material and have the instructor approve it.
2. Cut out the stock as listed in the bill of material.

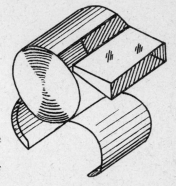

Fig. 18

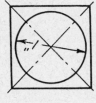

Fig. 19

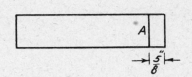

Fig. 20

Disk

3. Lay out the disks, drawing diagonal lines to locate the center (Fig. 19).
4. Carefully cut out the circle with a hand snips and, if necessary, file the edges smooth.

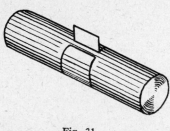

Fig. 21

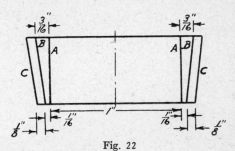

Fig. 22

Circle

5. Lay out line *A* shown in Figure 20.
6. Bend the small portion at right angles to the rest of the piece.
7. Bend it around a piece of 1-in. bar iron (Fig. 21).

Mouthpiece

8. Lay out the lines shown in Figure 22 and draw them in the following order: the center line, then *A*, *B*, and *C*.

9. Cut along the lines marked *C*.

10. Make the right-angle bends along line *A*, Figure 23, over a stake.

11. With a needle-nose pliers make the bends along line *B*, Figure 24.

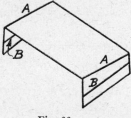

Fig. 23

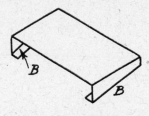

Fig. 24

Handle

12. Lay out the handle as shown in Figure 25. All lines are ¼ in. from the edge.

13. Cut off the corners which are shown as the shaded portions in Figure 25.

14. Make a double ⅛-in. hem parallel to both of the long sides (at *A* in Fig. 25).

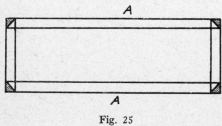

Fig. 25

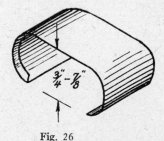

Fig. 26

15. With a stake or metal rod, round the ends as shown in Figure 26. The hems should be on the inside. The handle should be bent so that it will fit over the first and second fingers.

Assembly

16. Solder the disks on the inside edges of the circle. Be sure to put the dry pea on the inside of the cylinder before soldering the second disk in place. A round cork, which can be whittled with a knife, will function better than the dry pea.

17. Solder the mouthpiece and the handle in place (Fig. 18).

18. Wash off the surplus flux, clean the whistle with steel wool, and adjust the mouthpiece to secure the maximum volume.

REFERENCES

A. *Cold Metalwork Notebook*, Willoughby and Chamberlain (Bruce Publishing Co.).

B. *Metalwork Essentials*, Tustison and Kranzusch (Bruce Publishing Co.).

QUESTIONS

1. In what form is solder offered for sale? How is it sold? (Ref. A, p. 14.)
2. What is the value of a pair of 6-in. dividers. Check the price in a tool catalogue.
3. Describe the circumference rule and tell where it is used (Ref. B, p. 2).
4. Give the nearest U. S. Standard Gauge equivalent to 1/32 in.; 1/16 in.; and ⅛ in. (Ref. B, p. 5.)
5. For what is the hawkbill snips used? (Ref. B, p. 15.)

AUTO ASH CONTAINER

This ash container, designed to hook on some handy place in the car, is readily emptied by sliding the body upward. It is possible to attach a small rubber suction cup to the back of the container so that it may be attached to the car window.

MATERIALS REQUIRED

Front — 1 piece, IX tin plate, 2⅜ by 4⅛ in.
Sides — 2 pieces, IX tin plate, 1 7/16 by 2⅝ in.
Base — 1 piece, 22-ga. black iron (cut later).
Hook — 1 piece, 22-ga. black iron, ½ by 1⅛ in.

DIRECTIONS

1. Make out a bill of material and have the instructor approve it.
2. Cut out the materials listed above.

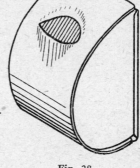

Fig. 28

Sides

3. Lay out the sides as shown in Figure 29 and draw the lines in the following order: *A*, circle *B*, and diagonals *C*.

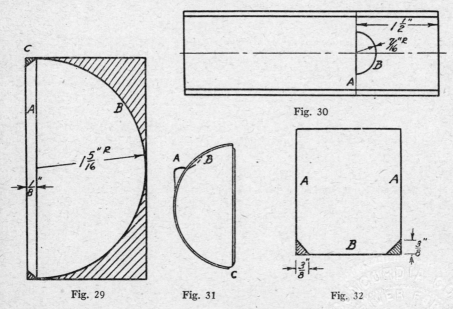

Fig. 30

Fig. 29   Fig. 31   Fig. 32

4. Check the layout and cut out the shaded portions shown in Figure 29.
5. With a bar folder set at 90 deg., bend the portion *A* in Figure 29 at right angles.
6. Lay out the front as shown in Figure 30 and draw the lines in the following order: center line *A*, and then the semicircle *B*.

7. With a piercing saw, cut out the semicircle just drawn. Make the edges smooth with a jewelers' file.

8. Turn a double ⅛-in. hem along both sides (Fig. 30).

9. With a slip-form roller bend the piece into a half circle. Be sure that the hem is on the inside. As you form the piece into shape, keep trying the sides until they fit evenly.

10. With a ball-peen hammer and a lead block, form the lips of the semicircle. The lower flat lip is tapped out (*A* in Fig. 31) and the upper round lip is tapped in (*B* in Fig. 31).

11. Solder the sides in place inside of the hem with a bottoming soldering copper. Solder one side at a time. Do not forget to provide space so that the ash container will slide into the hem of the base (*C*, in Fig. 31).

Base

12. Cut the base 2 13/16 in. long and ⅜ in. wider than the back of the container just soldered. The measurement should be taken across the widest portion.

13. Lay out the base as shown in Figure 32 and cut out the shaded portions.

14. With a bar folder set at ⅛ in., turn the open hems along sides *A* in Figure 32. The ash receiver should slide in this track.

15. With the bar folder at the same setting, turn edge *B* to an angle of 90 deg. and in the same direction as the hems just turned.

Hook

16. Lay out the hook as shown in Figure 33, and bend it to shape.

17. Fasten it in place on the back of the base. It can be either soldered, welded, or riveted.

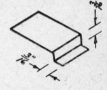

Fig. 33

Finish

18. The ash container can be finished as desired, but a crystal paint is recommended.

REFERENCES

A. *Materials of Industry*, Mersereau (McGraw-Hill).

B. *Dictionary of Technical Terms*, Crispin (Bruce Publishing Co.).

C. *Metalwork Essentials*, Tustison and Kranzusch (Bruce Publishing Co.).

QUESTIONS

1. Why is tin used in coating so-called "tin cans"? (Ref. A, p. 473.)

2. List five commercial uses of tin (Ref. A, p. 475).

3. Describe a semicircle (Ref. B).

4. How long would you cut a piece of tin plate for a cooky cutter 3½ in. in diameter? Allow ⅛ in. for an overlap (Ref. C, p. 119).

5. What is a flux and what part does it play in the soldering process? (Ref. C, p. 21.)

23158

WINDMETER

Here is a device for your bicycle that the wind will rotate with great speed. If so desired, it may be made larger so that it may be mounted on a house, barn, or fence.

MATERIALS REQUIRED

Small Windmeter

Spinner — 1 piece, 4½ by 4½-in. IX tin plate.
Spacer — 1 piece, ½ by 2½-in. dowel.
Support — 1 piece, 1/16 by ½ by 4-in. wrought iron.
Clamp — 1 piece, 1/16 by ½ by 7-in. wrought iron.

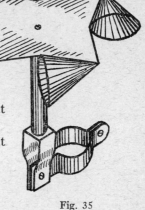

Large Windmeter

Spinner — 1 piece, 8¾ by 8¾-in. IX tin plate.
Spacer — 1 piece, ⅛ by ½ by 9½-in. wrought iron.
Support — 1 piece, 1/16 by ½ by 4-in. wrought iron.

Fig. 35

DIRECTIONS

Spinner

1. Make out a bill of material and have the instructor approve it.
2. Cut out the materials as they are listed.

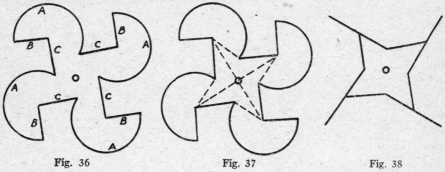

Fig. 36   Fig. 37   Fig. 38

3. Make a pattern of the spinner and trace the outline to the metal (Fig. 36).

4. Cut the outline as directed in Figure 36 with a straight snips in the following order: curves *A,* straight lines *B,* and finally straight lines *C.*

5. Draw the lines shown in Figure 37. Rest the metal on a wood block and with a No. 9 solid punch, punch the center hole at *O.*

6. Bend all the curved parts sharply down at a 90-deg. angle along the dotted lines (Figs. 37 and 38).

7. Form the cones with a small pliers (Fig. 35).

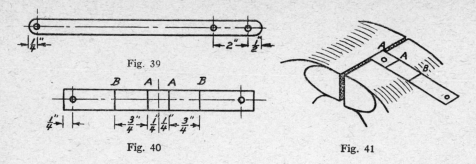

Fig. 39

Fig. 40

Fig. 41

8. Solder the inside junction of the cone ends. The joints must be tight before beginning to solder.

Spacer (small meter)

9. Smooth and square the ends of the spacer.

10. Locate the centers of both ends and make a No. 34 hole about ½ in. deep with a hand drill.

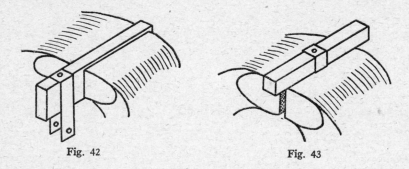

Fig. 42

Fig. 43

Spacer (large meter)

11. Grind both ends of the stock round with a power grinder.

12. Lay out the holes shown in Figure 39.

13. Center punch each and drill 3/16-in. holes. Smooth off the burrs.

Support (same for large and small models)

14. Make both ends of the piece square with a file (Fig. 40).

15. Lay out the lines in Figure 40 in the following order: center line, lines *A*, lines *B*, and finally all holes.

16. Center punch the hole locations and drill them with a 3/16-in. drill on a power drill press.

17. Clamp the support in a vise and bend it along line *A* in Figure 41.

18. Clamp the ½-in. bar in position as shown in Figure 42 and bend it accordingly.

19. Set the ½ by ½-in. block in place and squeeze it into position (Fig. 43).

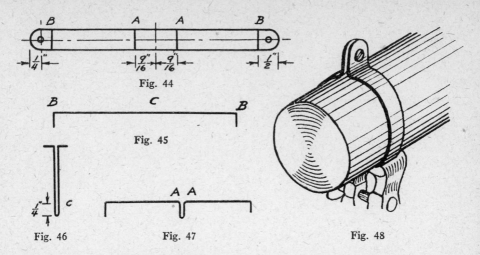

Fig. 44

Fig. 45

Fig. 46   Fig. 47   Fig. 48

Clamp (for small windmeter)

20. Round both ends of the clamp on a power grinder (Fig. 44).

21. Lay out the lines shown in Figure 44 in the following order: *A, B.*

22. Center punch the holes and drill them with a 3/16-in. bit.

23. Make a bend along lines *B* so that the ends face down (Fig. 45).

24. Bend the piece double at the center line (Fig. 46).

25. Drill hole *C* in Figure 46 with a 3/16-in. bit.

26. Bend down on line *A* so that the piece appears as shown in Figure 47.

27. Clamp it in a hand vise (Fig. 47), and bend the model over a stake. When the ends come together, put a bolt through the holes and finish the rounding (Fig. 48).

Assembly

28. Secure all of the necessary nuts and bolts.

29. Assemble the meter as shown in Figure 35.

30. Clean it with steel wool.

31. If the meter is to be painted with more than one color, allow the first coat to dry before applying the second.

REFERENCES

A. *School and Home Shopwork,* Schultz and Schultz (Allyn and Bacon).

B. *Essentials of Metal Working,* Berg and Wing (Manual Arts Press).

QUESTIONS

1. Upon what does the size of a solid punch depend? (Ref. A, p. 205.)

2. "Mechanical drawing is the language of industry." What is the meaning of this statement? (Ref. A, p. 6.)

3. Name four kinds of tin snips (Ref. A, p. 194).

4. Why must metal parts to be soldered be clean? (Ref. B, p. 194.)

5. What is the greatest danger in handling sheet metals? How can it be remedied?

WEATHER VANE

The main cylinder or housing of this weather vane is made from a discarded tin can.

MATERIALS REQUIRED

Body — a discarded tin can about 4¾ in. in diameter and 5 in. high.
Fin — 1 piece, 4½ by 5-in. IX tin plate.
Roof — 1 piece, 8 by 8-in. IX tin plate.
Propellers — 4 pieces, 1¾ by 4-in. IX tin plate.
Propeller support — 1 piece, 4 by 4-in. galvanized sheet iron.
Shaft — 1 piece, 14 in. long, No. 5 wire.
Mounting — 1 piece, ⅛ by ¾ by 12-in. wrought iron.

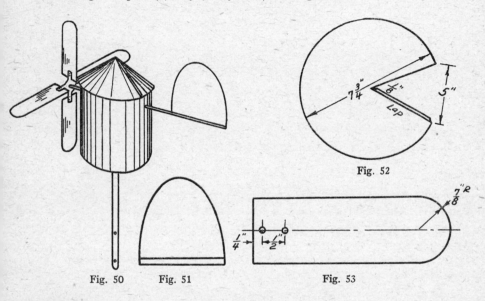

Fig. 50   Fig. 51   Fig. 52   Fig. 53

DIRECTIONS

1. Make out a bill of material and have the instructor approve it. Cut out the material as listed.

Body

2. Procure a tin can of the required size and locate the center of the bottom.

3. Punch a hole at this location with a punch having 3/16-in. face.

4. Mark the locations where the shaft will pass through the cylinder 1 in. below the top and punch it with a 3/16-in. solid punch (Fig. 50).

Fin

5. Lay out the elliptical form shown in Figure 51. Cut it out with a tinner's snips and smooth off the burrs.

6. Set the bar folder for the $\frac{1}{4}$-in. shaft and make an open fold along the bottom edge (Fig. 51).

Roof

7. Make a layout as shown in Figure 52. Cut it out with a tinner's snips and smooth off the burrs.

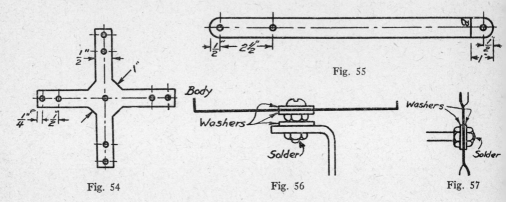

Fig. 55

Fig. 54

Fig. 56

Fig. 57

8. The cone shape of the roof is formed by hand over a stake of the proper shape. The hem should overlap $\frac{1}{8}$ in. so that it may be soldered.

9. Solder the roof along the hem.

Propeller

10. The four pieces for the propeller are laid out as shown in Figure 53. Cut them out with a tin snips and smooth off the burrs.

11. Locate the holes shown in Figure 53 and punch them with a No. 9 solid punch.

Propeller Support

12. Lay out the support as shown in Figure 54. Cut it out with a tin snips and smooth off the burrs.

13. Locate the holes shown in Figure 54 and center punch them.

14. Punch the eight small holes with a No. 9 solid punch. Drill the center hole large enough to turn free in the shaft.

Shaft

15. Cut a piece of wire or rod for the shaft; file the ends flat; and be sure that the shaft is exactly straight.

16. With a 10–24 die (check the size with the instructor), thread one end of the shaft for a distance of $\frac{1}{2}$ in.

Mounting

17. Cut the wrought-iron mounting and round both ends on a power grinder (Fig. 55).

18. Locate the holes shown in Figure 55, center punch them, and drill with a 3/16-in. drill.

19. Bend the portion above the line *B* at right angles to the main portion of the mounting (Fig. 55).

20. The weather vane may be put together with 1-lb. rivets. *Cold Metal Working,* by Van Leuven, gives the classification of tinner's rivets.

21. Rivet the four propellers to the support.

22. Bend the propeller mounting below each blade to a 45-deg. angle so that the wind will catch it (Fig. 50).

23. Assemble the mounting to the body (Fig. 56). After making certain that the body turns freely, cut the bolt below the last nut. Then smooth it with a file and solder it.

24. Fasten the fin to the end of the shaft on a wiring machine, and make it secure with solder.

25. Slip the shaft through the body, center the fin, and solder the shaft to the body.

26. Assemble the propeller (Fig. 57). Solder the back nut first and then slip on the washers and the propeller; and finally adjust the front nut and cut off the surplus stock. Solder it fast.

27. Solder the roof to the top of the body in four or six places.

28. Clean off the entire vane with emery cloth and steel wool.

29. Before enameling check the colors with the instructor.

REFERENCES

A. *School and Home Shopwork,* Schultz and Schultz (Allyn and Bacon).

B. *Metal Work,* Jones (Bruce Publishing Co.).

C. *Essentials of Metal Work,* Berg and Wing (Manual Arts Press).

QUESTIONS

1. How are files classified? (Ref. C, p. 35.)

2. Give the method of drawing iron wire (Ref. B, p. 14).

3. This project utilizes one of the millons of tin cans wasted every year. Suggest some remedy to relieve this waste.

4. Why is copper used for a soldering bit? (Ref. B, p. 66.)

5. In your estimation, give three evidences of a tidy worker.

BOOK ENDS

Made from a single piece of black sheet iron, this enameled book end is a welcome addition to anyone's desk. The large flat bottom assures stability. The turned bead is not only ornamental but also adds to the rigidity.

BILL OF MATERIAL

2 pieces, 5 by 9-in. 22-ga. black sheet iron.

DIRECTIONS

1. Make out a bill of material and have the instructor approve it.

2. Cut out the material as directed above.

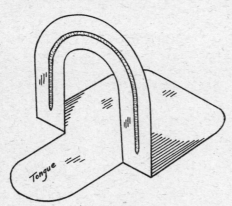

Fig. 59   Fig. 60

3. Lay out both pieces as shown in Figure 60. Draw the lines in the following order: center line A; curve B; curve C; curves D; and finally lines E.

4. Cut out along the outside curves B and D in Figure 60.

5. File the edges smooth and be sure to keep the part being filed close to the vise jaws.

6. In order to cut out the tongue (Fig. 59), clamp the piece of metal in a vise as shown in Figure 61. With a cold chisel and a hammer, make a cut along the first straight line only. See the instructor for a demonstration, and see also the picture in the center of the Stanley Chart, C53.

7. After cutting the first straight line, continue chiseling along the curve. It is important to shift the work continually so that the spot being chiseled is always just above the vise jaws.

8. After finishing the curve, continue on the other straight line. This will finish the entire tongue.

9. Then place the piece in a vise and bend it forward (Fig. 62). Use the hands for the first bend and finish it with a mallet. Test it for squareness.

10. File the edges smooth, being especially careful of the bumps on the curve.

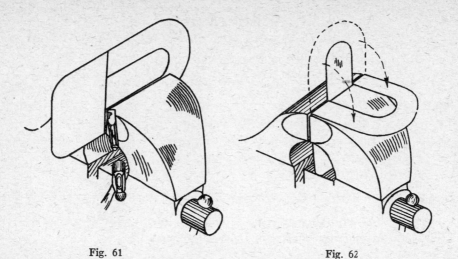

Fig. 61   Fig. 62

11. Roll the ornament shown in Figure 59 with a turning or beading roll (ask the instructor for aid).

12. Smooth out any snarls in the metal, which were caused by rolling, with a mallet and a hammer.

13. Clean off the book ends with emery cloth.

14. It is recommended that they be given a coat of dull enamel, but they may be finished as desired.

REFERENCES

A. Stanley Tool Chart, C53, Educational Dept. (Stanley Rule and Level Plant.)

B. Any Standard Dictionary.

C. *Essentials of Metalworking,* Berg and Wing (Manual Arts Press).

D. *Metalwork Essentials,* Tustison and Kranzusch (Bruce Publishing Co.).

QUESTIONS

1. In the introductory paragraph we speak of stability. What do you understand by this? (Ref. B.)

2. How do the flat chisel and the cape chisel differ in usage? (Ref. A or Ref. C, p. 34.)

3. List three different ways in which a flat or cold chisel may be used (Ref. A or Ref. D, pp. 81 to 84).

4. What kind of file would you use for the following metals: soft steel, hard steel, aluminum, lead? (Ref. D, p. 90.)

5. Give the route and final destination of most of the iron ore shipped from Duluth and other iron shipping centers on the Great Lakes (Ref. D, p. 167).

BED LAMP

While this project is intended primarily as a bed lamp, it can be put to many other uses. If the brackets are bent flat, the lamp can be adapted to a shelf, desk, or perhaps some sort of display.

BILL OF MATERIAL

Shade — 1 piece, 9 by 10¼-in. IX tin plate.
Ends — 2 pieces, 3½ by 4¼-in. IX tin plate.
Socket bracket — 1 piece, 2 by 2¾-in. 18-ga. black iron.
Hooks — 2 pieces, 1/16 by ½ by 6½-in. wrought iron.

DIRECTIONS

1. Make out a bill of material and have the instructor approve it.
2. Cut out the materials as listed above.

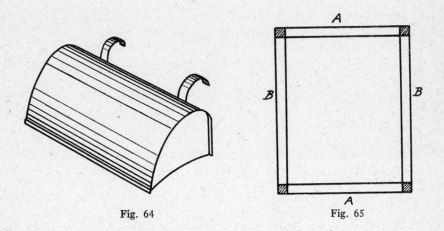

Fig. 64   Fig. 65

Ends

3. Trace the outline of the pattern to the metal.
4. Cut the endpieces out carefully and, if necessary, smooth the edges with a file.

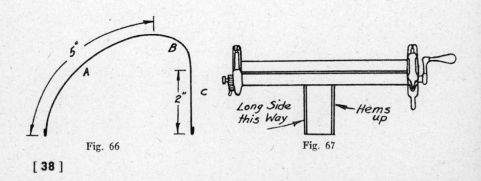

Fig. 66   Fig. 67

[38]

Shade

5. Draw lines 7/16 in. from the edge on all sides (Fig. 65).

6. Cut the shaded sections in Figure 65.

7. On the edges marked *A*, turn a double 3/16-in. hem in the same direction. On the edges marked *B*, turn a double 3/16-in. in the opposite direction from the hems marked *A*.

8. Measure off 5 in. for curve *A* shown in Figure 66. Bend this portion in the form roller until it fits the curve on the endpieces. Be sure the shade is fed through the rolls as shown in Figure 67.

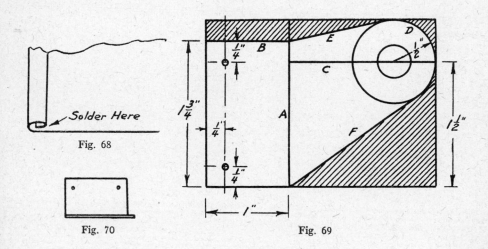

Fig. 68

Fig. 70

Fig. 69

9. Curve *B* may be formed on a stake or any round surface 2½ in. in diameter. The remaining portion *C* remains straight.

10. After the ends are fitted, solder them in place on the inside (Fig. 68). Begin the soldering on the gradual curve and work around to the straight part.

Socket Bracket

11. Lay out the piece of metal as shown in Figure 69, drawing the lines in the following order: *A, B, C*, circle *D, E*, and *F*.

12. After checking with the instructor, cut out the shaded portions.

13. Lay out the holes (Fig. 69). The large hole is made with a 13/32-in. punch and the two small ones with a ⅛-in. drill.

14. Bend the diagonal portion of the bracket at right angles (Fig. 70).

Hooks

15. Drill a ⅛-in. hole at *A* only, ½ in. from the bottom of each piece (Fig. 71).

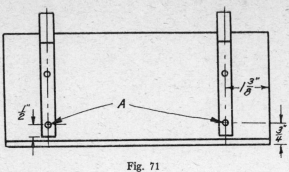

Fig. 71

16. Clamp the socket bracket (already drilled) and both hooks together in a hand vise after slipping a rivet through the holes of all three pieces to hold them in line. Drill ⅛-in. holes through both pieces.

17. Bend both hooks over a stake 2 in. in diameter (Fig. 71), any size you desire.

Assembly

18. Draw both center lines on the back of the shade (Fig. 71).

19. Punch the bottom hole only through the shade with a No. 9 solid punch. These holes should be ¾ in. from the bottom of the shade (Fig. 71).

20. Locate the top hole by setting the hook in place, slipping in a rivet, and scribing the location of the hole on a center line. Punch them in the same manner as given in the preceding direction.

21. Rivet all of the parts together with either 1-lb. tinner's rivets or ⅛ by ½-in. iron rivets. Be sure the socket bracket is in place, the inside on the right.

22. Connect the wire, socket, and plug.

23. Since the shade is made from tin plate, it can be polished with fine steel wool. The heat of the bulb will burn ordinary paint or enamel. The brackets, however, can be painted.

REFERENCES

A. *General Shop Metal Work,* A. W. and K. L. Dragoo (McKnight and McKnight).

B. *Cold Metalwork Notebook,* Willoughby and Chamberlain (Bruce Publishing Co.).

C. *School and Home Shopwork,* Schultz and Schultz (Allyn and Bacon).

D. *Metalwork Essentials,* Tustison and Kranzusch (Bruce Publishing Co.).

QUESTIONS

1. Explain some of the precautions that must be taken in forming sheet metal (Ref. A, p. 46).

2. What do we mean by a 2-lb. copper? (Ref. A, p. 51.)

3. How is it possible to measure the length of stock necessary for the portion of the lamp shade curving around the shade end? (Ref. B, p. 16.)

4. Name six general products made from sheet metal (Ref. C, pp. 190–191).

5. Give a general use for each of the following metals: copper, lead, tin, aluminum, zinc, and pewter (Ref. D, pp. 158–164).

[40]

DESK LAMP

This lamp is very popular because it is one that most anybody can use. While it is intended mainly as a desk lamp, it can be used in many other places.

MATERIALS REQUIRED

Reflector — 1 piece, 6¾ by 7-in. No. 26 black sheet iron.

U frame — 1 piece, ⅛ by ⅝ by 18½-in. wrought iron.

Base — 1 piece, 4¼ by 9-in., 18- or 22-ga. black sheet iron.

Reflector ends — 2 pieces, 3¼ by 3¼-in., No. 26 black sheet iron.

DIRECTIONS

1. Make out a bill of material and have the instructor approve it.

2. Cut out the materials as listed.

Reflector Ends

3. With a divider, draw the largest circle possible on both pieces (Fig. 74). Cut them off carefully with a tin snips and file off the burrs.

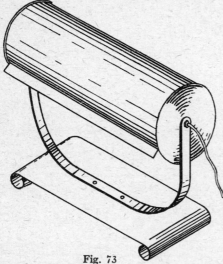

Fig. 73

4. As shown at *A* in Figure 74, drill a ⅛-in. hole in one piece. In the other piece punch a 13/32-in. hole.

5. With a raising block and hammer (No. 4 recommended) raise or cup both pieces approximately ¼ to ⅛ in.

6. After checking this with the instructor, turn a ⅛-in. burr on both pieces.

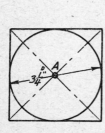

Fig. 74

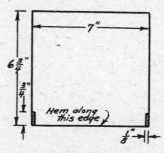

Fig. 75

Fig. 76

Fig. 77

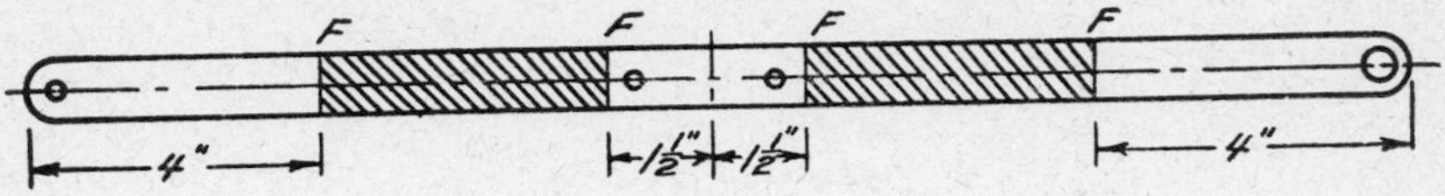

Fig. 78

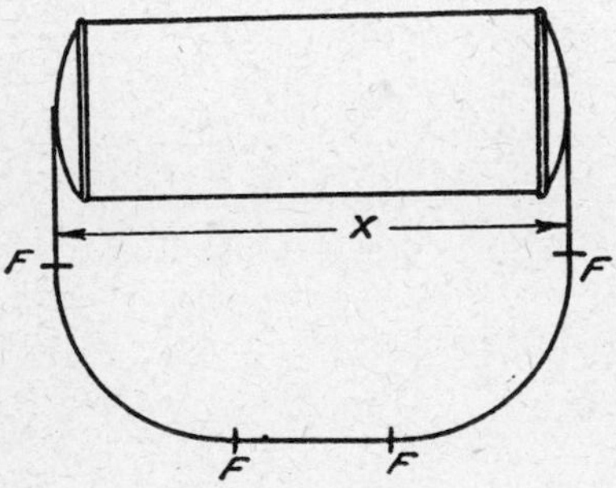

Fig. 79

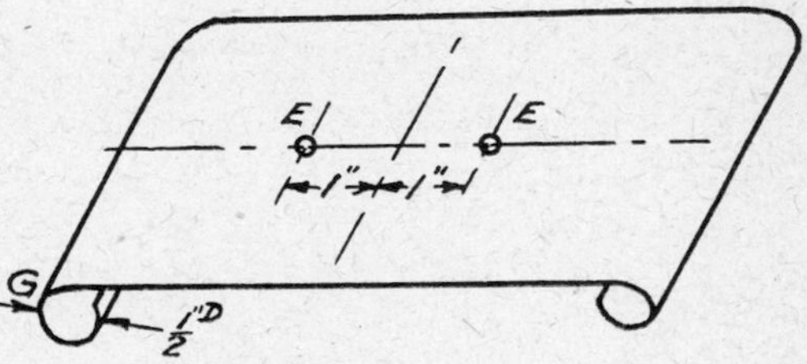

Fig. 80

Reflector

7. Lay out the notches shown in Figure 75. Be sure that they are in the right corners.

8. Notch the corners with a tin snips (Fig. 75).

9. With a bar folder, turn a single 3/16-in. hem along the notched edge (Fig. 75).

10. Using a slip form roller and with the hem on the inside, gradually form the cylinder. Keep trying the reflector endpieces to make sure of a snug fit.

11. With a hand seamer, or by clamping part B on a stake and using a mallet, bend this part out about 45 deg. from its original position. Be sure not to get the cylinder out of shape.

U Frame

12. Round both ends of the frame on a grinder (Fig. 77).

13. Lay out the holes shown in Figure 77.

14. With a ⅛-in. drill make the holes shown at C, and with a 13/32-in. drill at D.

15. Lay out the fold marks shown at F in Figure 78.

16. With a form roller or bending jig, bend the shaded sections shown at

F in Figure 78 until the U shape is reached as shown in Figure 79. The distance between *X* in Figure 79 should clamp the reflector ends snugly. The U piece should be square.

Base

17. Lay out the holes shown at *E* in Figure 80.

18. Check them so that they line up with the holes in the U piece. Make these holes with a ⅛-in. drill.

19. Form both ends of the base by bending them around a ½-in. round iron rod held in a vise (at *G* in Fig. 80). See the instructor for a demonstration.

Assembly

20. Fasten the reflector ends to the U frame in the following order: one end is fastened with ⅛-in. roundhead, black iron rivets; the other end should be fastened in place with a piece of ⅛-in. threaded pipe nipple, lock nut, and socket cap.

21. Rivet the U frame to the base with ⅛-in. roundhead, black iron rivets.

22. Finish the lamp as desired. It is recommended that the inside be painted with aluminum paint.

REFERENCES

A. *General Metal Shop,* Dragoo, A. W. and K. L. (McKnight and McKnight).

B. *Essentials in Metal Working,* Berg and Wing (Manual Arts Press).

C. *Metalwork Essentials,* Tustison and Kranzusch (Bruce Publishing Co.).

QUESTIONS

1. Give two purposes of a hem in sheet-metal working.

2. Give some information relative to the manufacture and use of emery cloth (Ref. A, p. 29).

3. Give the location and principal sources of iron ore in the United States (Ref. A, p. 30).

4. Explain the relationship between raising and the property of metal called malleability (Ref. B, p. 67).

5. Why are the so-called tin cans not pure tin? (Ref. C, p. 162.)

SECTION II

ART-METAL PROJECTS

NAME PLATE

This name plate will serve as a very good means of identification on the front door. It may also be used on a box or a chest. The most important item to watch is its design.

MATERIALS REQUIRED

1 piece, 18-ga. copper or brass, the size of the design.

DIRECTIONS

1. Get a sheet of squared paper from the instructor and draw the design, keeping in mind the following points:

   a) Draw the design with a ruler and a sharp-pointed pencil.
   b) Follow the lines on the paper wherever possible.
   c) Make an original design, using the drawings on this sheet only as a starting point.
   d) The name plate will look better if it has an etched border.

Fig. 82

Fig. 83

Fig. 84

2. Have the instructor check the design. Remember that this is the most important part of the plate.

3. Cut the metal to the correct length and width. Clean the surface with steel wool so that it will take carbon-paper marks.

4. Transfer the design to the metal with carbon paper. The pencil must have a sharp point; a scriber may be used, but be careful not to cut the paper.

5. Go over the design on the metal with a scriber after removing the carbon paper. Reclean it with steel wool.

6. Then cover all parts of the plate with asphaltum paint that are not to be cut by the acid.

7. Prepare the acid (see *Metal Work,* Jones, p. 44). Report on this method to the instructor.

8. After the asphaltum paint has dried, put the plate in the acid until it has been etched deeply enough. Check with the instructor. *Danger notice:* The acid is harmful. Do not splash any on yourself or your clothing. If this should happen accidentally, call the instructor.

9. Clean off the asphaltum paint with steel wool dampened with turpentine or kerosine.

10. Cut the name plate to size and file the edges smooth.

11. Locate the holes for mounting the plate. Center punch and make them with a ⅛-in. drill.

12. Reclean the plate with steel wool, holding it with a paper towel in order to prevent fingerprints. If the plate is made of copper, it may be colored by placing it in a liver of sulphur solution until the desired color is obtained. Rinse it with water and blot it dry. If you would like to polish the plate, see the instructor.

13. Finish the plate with a coat of lacquer to preserve the color.

REFERENCES

A. *Copper Work,* Rose (Metal Crafts Publishing Co.).
B. *Metal Work,* Jones (Bruce Publishing Co.).
C. *School and Home Workshop,* Schultz and Schultz (Allyn and Bacon).

QUESTIONS

1. Give your idea of the meaning of etching (Ref. B, p. 42).
2. Why are art-metal projects lacquered and how is it done? (Ref. B, p. 50.)
3. What is an alloy? (Ref. C, p. 193.)
4. Bronze was used by the ancients — how did they make it? (Ref. C, p. 193.)
5. Are the fumes from the etching solution dangerous? Why?

WATCH FOB

If made of heavy copper, these fobs serve their purpose the best. If drilled with a single hole, they can be used for identification tags. The most important part is the design.

MATERIALS REQUIRED

1 piece, 14-ga. 48-oz. copper, the size of the design.

DIRECTIONS

1. Get a sheet of squared paper from the instructor and draw a design, keeping in mind the following points:

   a) Use a ruler and sharp-pointed pencil for the drawing.
   b) Follow the lines on the squared paper wherever possible.
   c) Try to make an original design, or else make use of the reference books at the end of this project.
   d) Most fobs look better if they have an etched border.

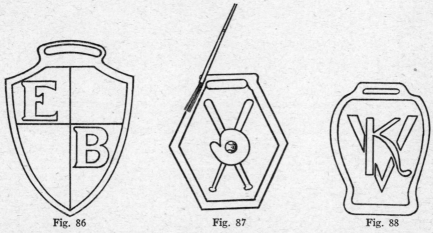

Fig. 86   Fig. 87   Fig. 88

2. Have the instructor check the design. Remember that the design is most important and that the designs shown are only a few of those possible.

3. Cut the metal to the correct length and width and clean it off with steel wool.

4. Transfer the design to the copper with carbon paper. The pencil must have a very sharp point. A scriber may be used, but care must be taken not to cut the paper.

5. Go over the design on the metal with a scriber after removing the carbon paper, and reclean it with steel wool.

6. Cover all parts of the fob with asphaltum paint that are not to be cut by the acid.

7. Prepare the acid (*Metal Work*, Jones, p. 44). Check this with the instructor.

8. When the asphaltum paint has dried, put the fob in the acid until it is etched deeply enough. *Danger notice:* Acid is harmful. Do not splash any on yourself or clothing. If this should happen accidentally, call the instructor.

9. Clean off the asphaltum paint with steel wool dampened with kerosine or turpentine.

10. Lay out the slot for the strap and drill a 1/16-in. hole at each end.

11. Cut the fob to size and file all the edges smooth.

12. Cut out the slot with a jewelers' saw and smooth it with a jewelers' file.

13. Reclean the fob with steel wool holding it with a paper towel in order to prevent finger prints.

14. In order to color the fob, if it is made of copper, put it in a liver of sulphur solution until the desired color is obtained. Rinse it with water and blot it dry.

15. Wipe it off lightly with a clean cloth and lacquer it to preserve the finish.

REFERENCES

A. *Art Metal Work*, Adams (Popular Mechanics Co.).
B. *Art Monograms and Lettering*, Bergling (J. M. Bergling).
C. *Metal Work*, Jones (Bruce Publishing Co.).
D. *Copper Work*, Rose (Metal Crafts Publishing Co.).
E. *Art Metal Work*, Payne (Manual Arts Press).

QUESTIONS

1. What acid is used in mixing an etching solution? (Ref. C, p. 44.)
2. Discuss briefly the uses of copper (Ref. C, p. 54).
3. Where was the first copper in the United States found and in what year? (Ref. E, p. 16.)
4. Give a safety rule in handling etching acid.
5. What is the difference between ornament and design? (Ref. E, p. 46.)

ETCHED BRACELET

A bracelet with an etched design makes a very nice gift. The number of designs possible are unlimited, depending on your own desires as to what you want on the bracelet. Do not forget that the most important item is the design.

MATERIALS REQUIRED

1 piece, 18-ga. copper, brass, or German silver, the length and width of the design.

DIRECTIONS

1. Get a sheet of squared paper from the instructor and make the design, keeping in mind the following instructions:

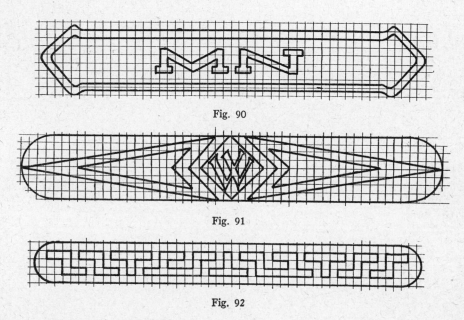

Fig. 90

Fig. 91

Fig. 92

a) Use a ruler and sharp-pointed pencil for the drawing.

b) Be sure to get the length of the bracelet by fitting a narrow band of paper around the wrist for which it is intended. The paper should be ½ in. from closing.

c) In drawing, follow the lines of the paper wherever possible.

d) Try to make an original design. Either use the drawings on this sheet or ask the instructor for more designs.

e) An etched bracelet generally looks better if the border is etched.

2. Have the instructor check the design. Remember that the design is the most important part of the job, and that the ones shown are but a few of the possibilities.

3. Cut the metal to the correct length and width and clean it off with steel wool.

4. Transfer the design to the metal with carbon paper. The pencil should have a very sharp point; a scriber may be used but care must be taken not to cut the paper.

5. Go over the design on the metal with a scriber after removing the carbon paper. Reclean the metal with steel wool.

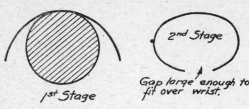

1st Stage

2nd Stage

Gap large enough to fit over wrist.

Fig. 93

6. With asphaltum paint, cover all parts of the job that are not to be cut by the acid.

7. Prepare the acid (*Metal Work*, Jones, p. 44).

8. When the asphaltum paint has dried, place the bracelet in the acid until it is etched deeply enough. Check this with the instructor. *Danger notice:* Acid is harmful. Do not splash any on yourself or your clothing. If this should happen accidentally, call the instructor.

9. Clean off the asphaltum paint with steel wool dampened with kerosine or turpentine.

10. Cut the bracelet to size and file it smooth.

11. Shape the bracelet over a stake with a mallet. Two stages are required for this process (Fig. 93).

12. Reclean the job with steel wool, holding it with a paper towel to avoid finger marks.

13. If the job is to be polished, use a buffer. A copper bracelet may be colored by immersing it in a liver of sulphur solution until the desired color is obtained. Rinse it with water and blot it dry.

14. Wipe it off very lightly with a clean cloth and give it a coat of lacquer to preserve the finish.

REFERENCES

A. *Metal Work,* Jones (Bruce Publishing Co.).

B. *Art Metal Work,* Payne (Manual Arts Press).

QUESTIONS

1. What is liver of sulphur? How is it used in connection with art-metal work? (Ref. A, p. 50.)

2. From where do the largest quantities of copper come? (Ref. B, p. 17.)

3. Give two methods for cleaning copper (Ref. A, p. 50).

4. What is copper oxide? (Ref. A, p. 50.)

5. Give four standards by which design is judged (Ref. B, p. 9).

SCOUT NECKERCHIEF SLIDE

Most scouts will welcome this etched neckerchief slide. Only a few of the possible designs are shown here, but by originating your own, you can get the effect you desire.

MATERIALS REQUIRED

1 piece, ¾ by 2⅜-in. 18-ga. copper, brass, or German silver.

DIRECTIONS

Fig. 95

1. If you want to use one of the designs on this page, draw it on a piece of metal. It is a much better idea, however, to make your own design according to the following directions:

  a) Get a piece of squared paper from the instructor.
  b) Make the drawing with ruler and sharp-pointed pencil.
  c) Follow the lines on the paper wherever possible.
  d) These slides look-better if they have an etched border.

Fig. 96

Fig. 97

2. Have the instructor check the design. Remember that the designs shown on this page are only a few of those possible.

3. Cut a piece of 18-ga. metal to the correct length and width and clean it off with steel wool.

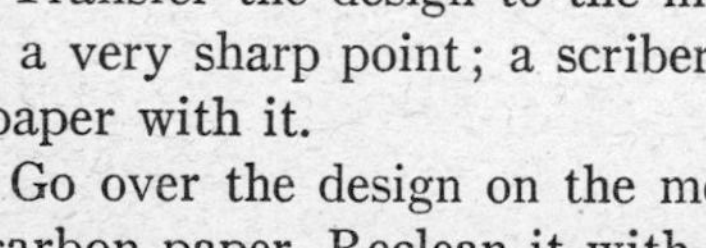

Fig. 98

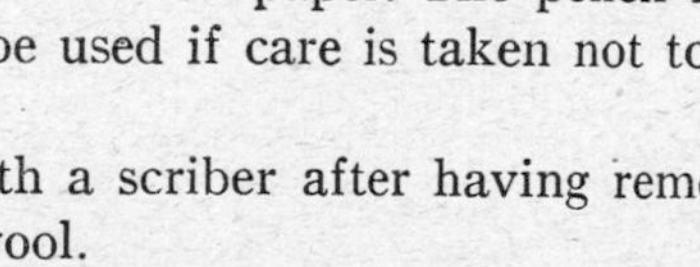

Fig. 99

4. Transfer the design to the metal with carbon paper. The pencil must have a very sharp point; a scriber may be used if care is taken not to cut the paper with it.

5. Go over the design on the metal with a scriber after having removed the carbon paper. Reclean it with steel wool.

6. Cover all parts of the job that are not to be cut by the acid with asphaltum paint.

7. After this paint has dried, scrape away any surplus with a razor blade.

8. Then put the slide into the acid until it has been etched to the proper

depth. *Danger notice:* Acid is harmful. Do not splash any of it on your skin or clothing. If this should happen accidentally, call the instructor.

9. Clean off the asphaltum paint with steel wool dampened slightly with kerosine or turpentine.

10. Shape the neckerchief slide over a round stake. Use a mallet and work it until you get a smooth cylinder (Fig. 95).

11. Reclean the slide with steel wool. Hold it with a paper towel in order to avoid fingerprints.

12. If the job is to be polished, do so on a buffer. If it is made of copper, it may be colored by immersing it in a liver of sulphur solution until the desired color is obtained. Then rinse it with water and blot it dry.

13. Wipe the slide off very lightly with a clean cloth and give it a coat of lacquer to preserve the finish.

REFERENCES

A. *Dictionary of Technical Terms,* Crispin (Bruce Publishing Co.).
B. *Metal Work,* Jones (Bruce Publishing Co.).

QUESTIONS

1. In polishing a job on a buffer, is it safer to hold it with a cloth or with a paper towel? Why?

2. What is a cylinder? (Ref. A.)

3. What is the purpose of the resist in etching? (Ref. B, p. 44.)

4. How is it possible to tell if the acid etching solution is of the correct strength? (Ref. B, p. 44.)

5. What is meant when it is said that the nitric acid is corrosive in action?

ETCHED PAPER KNIFE

Paper knives, sometimes called letter openers, are a welcome addition to any desk and oftentimes are a necessity. It would be much better to design a knife of your own, rather than use one of the designs shown here. One's initials or name, or perhaps some ornament can be very appropriately worked into the design.

MATERIALS REQUIRED

The material required should be decided after the design has been drawn. 18-ga. copper or brass may be used.

DIRECTIONS

1. If you want to use one of the designs shown here, transfer it to the metal with tracing paper. If you want to make your own design, some excellent ideas may be obtained from the references at the end of the instructions (Ref. A, pp. 4–5; Ref. B, p. 22; Ref. C, pp. 49–50; Ref. D, p. 21). Keep the following suggestions in mind:

   a) Get a sheet of squared paper and make the design.
   b) Make the drawing with a ruler and sharp-pointed pencil.
   c) Follow the lines of the paper wherever possible.
   d) Generally a paper knife will look better if it has some kind of a border.

2. Have the instructor check the design and remember that this is the most important part of the job.

3. Make out a bill of material and have the instructor approve it.

4. Cut out the material as listed above.

5. Transfer the design to the metal with carbon paper. Use a hard pencil with a sharp point. A scriber may be used, but care must be taken not to cut the paper.

6. After removing the carbon paper, go over the design on the metal with a scriber. Reclean the knife with steel wool.

7. Cover all parts of the knife that are not to be cut by the acid with asphaltum paint.

8. After that paint has dried, scrape off the excess with a razor blade.

9. Put the knife into the nitric acid etching solution until it has been etched deeply enough. *Danger notice:* The acid solution is harmful. Do not splash any on yourself or your clothing. If this should happen accidentally, call the instructor.

10. Clean off the asphaltum paint with steel wool dampened with kerosine or turpentine.

11. Cut the knife to size and file the edges smooth.

12. The cutting edge of the knife should be slightly filed. This may be done with a medium-cut file near the edge of the bench at the angle shown in Figure 104.

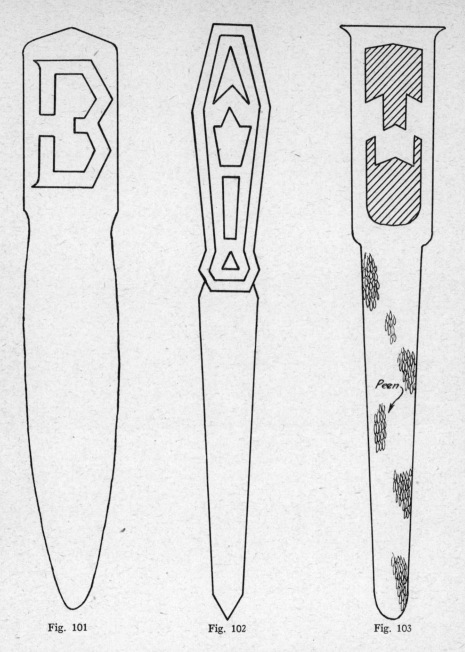

Fig. 101 Fig. 102 Fig. 103

13. Reclean the job with steel wool. Avoid finger marks by holding the job with a paper towel.

14. If the knife is to be polished, do so on a buffer. If it is made of copper, it may be colored by immersing it in a liver of sulphur solution until the desired color is obtained. Rinse it with water and blot it dry or place it in a sawdust barrel.

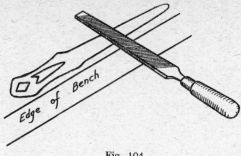

Fig. 104

15. Wipe it off lightly with a clean cloth and lacquer it to preserve the finish.

REFERENCES

A. *Art Metalwork — A Portfolio of Designs*, Rose (Metal Crafts Publishing Co.).

B. *Copper Work*, Rose (Metal Crafts Publishing Co.).

C. *Art Metalwork*, Payne (Manual Arts Press).

D. *Metalwork and Etching*, Adams (Popular Mechanics Co.).

E. *Metal Work*, Jones (Bruce Publishing Co.).

QUESTIONS

1. Give a safety rule for the handling of nitric acid.
2. Give your idea of the meaning of etching (Ref. E, p. 42).
3. Give four standards by which a design is judged (Ref. C, p. 9).
4. Give seven common primary shapes used in design (Ref. E, p. 46).
5. How can we tell if the acid etching solution is of the correct strength? (Ref. E, p. 44.)

ETCHED ROLLER BLOTTER

If you have a desk of your own or if some friend has one, this blotter will make a useful article.

MATERIALS REQUIRED

Top — 2 by 4-in. 18-ga. copper or brass.
Roller — 2 by 4½-in. 22-ga. copper or brass.

DIRECTIONS

1. Select the design for the roller blotter. The ones shown here are but a few of the possibilities. Why not make one of your own?

Fig. 106

2. Draw the design on a piece of squared paper with a ruler and sharp pencil. Be sure to follow the lines on the paper wherever possible and leave a 3/16-in. lip on each side to hold the roller (Figs. 106 and 107).

3. Have the instructor check the design. Remember that this is the most important part of the job.

Fig. 107

4. Cut the metal to the correct size and clean it off with steel wool.

5. Transfer the design to the metal with carbon paper and a very sharp pencil; a scriber may be used but care must be taken not to tear the paper.

6. After removing the carbon paper, go over the design on the metal with a scriber. Then reclean it with steel wool.

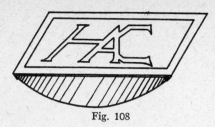

Fig. 108

7. Cover all parts of the job that are not to be cut by the acid with asphaltum paint.

8. When the asphaltum paint has dried, put the piece into the acid until it has been etched deeply enough. Avoid splashing acid on your body or clothing.

9. Clean off the asphaltum paint with steel wool dampened with kerosine or turpentine.

10. Set the bar folder at 3/16 in. and bend both ends at a 45-deg. angle (Fig. 108). This will allow the top to receive the roller.

11. Roll the brass piece in the form roller until it fits into the top of the roller blotter snugly (Fig. 108).

12. Reclean the holder with steel wool holding it with a paper towel to avoid fingerprints.

13. If the holder is to be polished, do so on a buffer.

14. If the top section is made of copper, it may be colored by placing it in a liver of sulphur solution until the desired color is obtained. Then rinse it with water and blot it dry or place it in sawdust. If the holder is made of brass, do not attempt to color it in the liver of sulphur solution; no noticeable change in color will result.

15. Polish it lightly with a clean cloth and give it a coat of lacquer to preserve the finish and the color.

REFERENCES

A. *Metal Working and Etching,* Adams (Popular Mechanics Co.).
B. *Art Metal Work,* Payne (Manual Arts Press).
C. *Metal Work,* Jones (Bruce Publishing Co.).
D. *Essentials of Metal Work,* Berg and Wing (Manual Arts Press).

QUESTIONS

1. In mixing an etching solution, give the correct procedure (Ref. C, p. 44).

2. Why do we put copper strips in the jaws of our vises for certain work?

3. Give seven common primary shapes used in design (Ref. C, p. 46).

4. What is the meaning of the word conductivity in regard to metals? (Ref. D, p. 68.)

5. Give three properties of copper (Ref. D, p. 70).

PUNCHED BRACELET — NAVAJO DESIGN

Nearly everyone of us has seen the bracelets and other forms of jewelry made by the Navajo Indians. This jewelry has its own distinctive beauty. All of the symbols have some meaning in the Indian sign language.

MATERIALS REQUIRED

1 piece, 18-ga. copper, brass, or German silver, ¾ in. by the distance around the wrist.

Fig. 110

DIRECTIONS

1. Measure the distance around the wrist with a narrow band of paper. The ends should be ½ in. apart.
2. Make out a bill of material and have the instructor approve it.
3. Cut out the metal.
4. If the ends are to be rounded, mark them carefully with a dividers.
5. Cut them out with a tin snips and file them smooth.
6. Clean the bracelet with steel wool and buff out all the scratches.
7. Decide on the design. There are many possibilities besides the one shown in Figure 110. Show the idea of the arrangement to the instructor and then try it out on a piece of scrap copper.
8. Carefully punch the design into the bracelet.
9. Form the bracelet to the wrist in two steps (Fig. 93).

   a) Form the entire bracelet into a partial circle over a stake with a mallet.
   b) Curve both ends on the stake.

10. Polish the bracelet on a buffer.
11. Give it a coat of lacquer to preserve the finish.

REFERENCES

A. *Handicraft — Simple Procedures and Projects,* Griswold (Lester Griswold).
B. *Dictionary of Technical Terms,* Crispin (Bruce Publishing Co.).
C. *Sheet Metal Worker's Manual,* Broemel (Frederick J. Drake).

QUESTIONS

1. Of what is German silver composed? (Ref. B.)
2. What do we mean when we say metal is malleable? (Ref. C, p. 445.)
3. Give the Indian interpretation of the symbols you put on your bracelet (Ref. A, p. 266).
4. Why don't we bend the bracelet exactly round?
5. Give a safety rule for the use of the buffer.

PUNCHED RING — NAVAJO DESIGN

The jewelry made by the Navajo Indians has a distinctive beauty all of its own. All of the symbols have some meaning in the Indian sign language.

MATERIALS REQUIRED

1 piece, ⅝ by 2⅝-in. 18-ga. copper, brass, or German silver.

DIRECTIONS

1. Make out a bill of material and have the instructor approve it.
2. Cut the material to the size listed above.
3. Draw the design for the ring (Ref. C, p. 226).
4. Scribe the outline of the ring from the pattern or design to the metal.
5. Cut it out with a snips and file it smooth. Use a vise with copper jaws and jewelers' file.
6. Clean it with steel wool and buff out all the scratches.
7. Punch the design on scrap metal; have the instructor approve it; and then punch it carefully into the ring blank.
8. Form the ring on the tail of a small stake (Fig. 113).
9. Cut off or file the ends to fit the finger for which it is intended.
10. The ring may be squeezed lightly in a vise to bring the ends together for soldering.
11. Polish the ring on a buffer and give it a coat of lacquer.

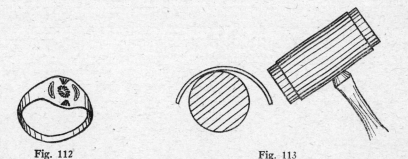

Fig. 112   Fig. 113

REFERENCES

A. *Metalwork Essentials*, Tustison and Kranzusch (Bruce Publishing Co.).

B. *Metalcraft and Jewelry*, Kronquist (Manual Arts Press).

C. *Handicraft — Simplified Procedures and Projects*, Griswold (Lester Griswold).

QUESTIONS

1. Why is flux used in soldering? (Ref. A, p. 21.)
2. What happens if the soldering copper becomes red hot? (Ref. A, p. 19.)
3. Give two methods for cutting out a ring blank (Ref. A, p. 15; Ref. B, p. 24).
4. Are punching dies made from hard steel? Why?
5. Why are soldering coppers made of copper? (Ref. A, p. 17.)

PEENED ROLLER BLOTTER

The peened design on the roller can be varied by using hammers that produce different indentions.

MATERIALS REQUIRED

Top — 1 piece, 2 by 5¼-in. 18-ga. brass, copper, or German silver.
Bottom — 1 piece, 2 by 5½-in., 18-ga. brass, copper, or German silver.
Handle — 1 piece, ½ by ⅜-in. brass, copper, or German silver rod.

DIRECTIONS

1. Make out a bill of material and have the instructor approve it.
2. Cut out the stock and have the instructor approve it.

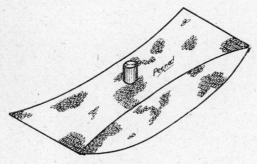

Fig. 115

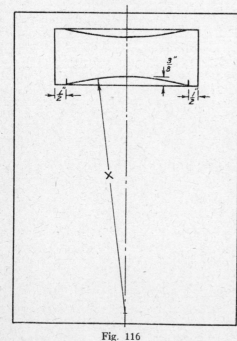

Fig. 116

Top

3. Lay out the curved sides of the top as follows:

   a) Draw a center line on the metal parallel to the short sides (Fig. 116).

   b) On a sheet of paper, 8½ by 11 in., draw the center line shown in Figure 116.

   c) Set the metal on the paper so that the center lines jibe.

   d) Adjust the dividers and draw the arc shown in Figure 116.

4. Cut out the arc with a curved snips and file the edges smooth.

5. Peen the roller with a hammer that will produce the desired marks.

6. Set a bar folder at a 45-deg. angle and bend the ends 3/16 in.

7. Lay out the hole for the center knob and drill it with a No. 27 drill.

Bottom

8. Peen the bottom piece with the same hammer that was used on the top.
9. Round the bottom to shape on a form so that the top fits tightly.

Handle

10. File the top and bottom of the handle square.
11. Locate the center of the top and punch it for drilling.
12. Secure a tap drill for a 6–32 machine screw.
13. Drill the hole deeply enough, but not through the piece.
14. Tap the hole with the 6–32 tap.

Assembly

15. Clean all the parts with steel wool. If the roller is made of copper it may be colored with liver of sulphur.
16. The roller may be polished on a buffer.
17. Screw the handle in place with a ¼-in., 6–32, roundhead, brass machine screw.
18. Give the entire roller a coat of clear lacquer.

REFERENCES

A. *Metalwork Essentials,* Tustison and Kranzusch (Bruce Publishing Co.).

B. *Cold Metalworking,* Van Leuven (McGraw-Hill).

QUESTIONS

1. Explain fully what is meant by the term, ½-in., 8–32, roundhead, brass machine screw (Ref. A, p. 132).
2. Give some information in regard to copper (Ref. A, p. 158).
3. Which is the larger: A No. 28 drill or a ⅛-in. drill? (Ref. B, p. 237.)
4. How is a tap started? (Ref. A, p. 134.)
5. Find out the price of a good pair of 6-in. dividers.

PAPER KNIFE

A good paper knife for opening letters is a necessary part of every desk set. Besides being of practical value after it is finished, its making allows the use of the jewelers' saw.

MATERIALS REQUIRED

18-ga. copper or brass, the size of the design.

DIRECTIONS

1. Decide on the design to be used.
2. Lay out the design on squared paper and if possible make an original one.
3. After the instructor has checked the design, cut a piece of metal to the correct size.
4. Transfer the design to the metal with carbon paper and a scriber. Then go over the carbon impression with the scriber.
5. Carefully cut out the outline of the knife with a snips and file it to shape. (If it is impossible to cut it with a snips, follow the directions for the use of the jewelers' saw in Directions 9 and 10 below.)
6. Near an end of the bench form a slight cutting edge on the knife with a medium-cut file.
7. The pierced portion of the knife should be center punched in each sharp corner. All center-punch marks must be inside of the line on which the sawing is to be done.
8. Drill a 1/16-in. hole at all of these locations.
9. Set up the saw and jig shown in Figure 123.

   a) The saw teeth must point toward the handle.
   b) Insert the blade into the clamp farthest from the handle.
   c) Put the blade through the hole in the knife.
   d) Tighten the blade in the clamp next to the handle.

10. Saw out the waste portions observing the following points:

    a) Turn the curves slowly, sawing all the while.
    b) Keep the blade tight.
    c) Do not twist the blade.
    d) Saw with a steady, slow stroke.

11. Carefully file out all the sawed portions with jewelers' files.
12. If the knife has a peened portion as well as a pierced one, or any chasing, do this now.
13. Clean it carefully with steel wool avoiding finger marks.
14. If the job is to be polished, do so on a buffer.
15. If the knife is made of copper, it may be colored by placing it in a

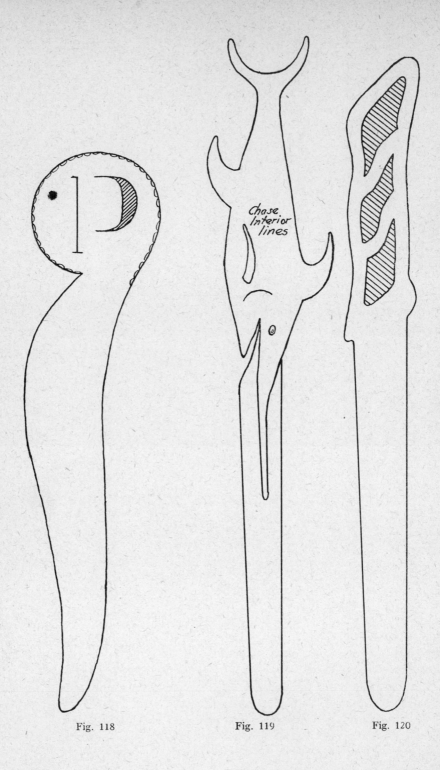

Chase
Interior
lines

Fig. 118   Fig. 119   Fig. 120

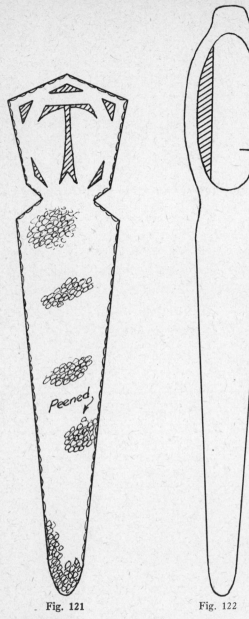

Fig. 121

Fig. 122

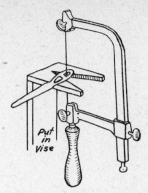

Fig. 123

liver of sulphur solution until
the desired color is obtained.
Rinse it with water and blot
it dry.

16. Polish the knife lightly
with a clean cloth and give it
a coat of lacquer.

REFERENCES

A. *Copper Work*, Rose
(Metal Crafts Publishing
Co.).

B. *Home Workshop Manual*, Wakeling (Popular
Science Publishing Co.).

C. *A Portfolio of Designs*,
Rose (Metal Crafts Publishing Co.).

D. *Art Metal Work*, Payne
(Manual Arts Press).

E. *Metal Work*, Jones
(Bruce Publishing Co.).

QUESTIONS

1. How is a jewelers' saw blade placed into a frame (Ref. D, p. 67).
2. How long should an object remain in a nitric acid etching solution?
(Ref. E, p. 44).
3. Give two methods for coloring copper (Ref. E, p. 50).
4. Give some of the properties of lead (Ref. E, p. 2).
5. How thick is 18-ga. copper? (Ref. D, p. 29).

PIERCED BOOKMARK

This will be a sturdy bookmark if made of 22-ga. brass or copper. It has a pierced design. Although you may receive some aid from the references below, it is much better to make your own design.

MATERIALS REQUIRED

22-ga. copper or brass, the size of the design.

DIRECTIONS

1. Decide on the design to be used.
2. Draw the design on squared paper and have the instructor approve it. Cut the metal to size.
3. Transfer the design to the metal with carbon paper and a scriber. Go over the carbon impression with a scriber.
4. Cut out the exterior outline with a snips and file it to shape. If the design is quite fine, it may be necessary to saw the outline.

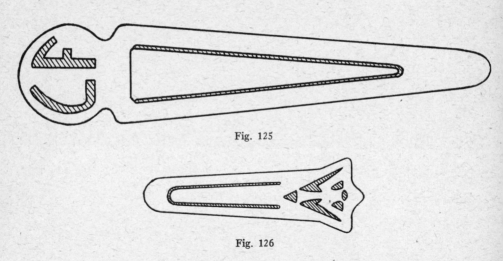

Fig. 125

Fig. 126

5. Center punch the design in each sharp corner of the portion to be cut. All center-punch marks must be 1/16 in. inside of the line to be sawed. These are the shaded portions of Figures 125 and 126.
6. Drill a 1/16-in. hole at all of these locations. All holes must be within the shaded areas shown in Figures 125 and 126.
7. Set up the saw and jig shown in Figure 123.

   a) The saw teeth must point toward the handle.
   b) Insert the blade into the clamp farthest from the handle.
   c) Put the blade through the hole in the bookmark.
   d) Tighten the end of the blade near the handle.

8. Saw out the waste portions observing the following rules:

a) Turn the curves slowly, sawing all the while.
b) Keep the blade tight.
c) Do not twist the blade.
d) Saw with a steady, slow stroke.

9. File out the sawed portions very carefully with jewelers' files.

10. Carefully clean the bookmark with steel wool and avoid finger marks.

11. If the job is to be polished use a buffer.

12. If the job is made of copper, it may be immersed in a liver of sulphur solution until the desired color is obtained. Rinse it with water and blot it dry.

13. Polish it lightly with a clean cloth and give it a coat of lacquer to preserve the finish.

REFERENCES

A. *A Portfolio of Designs,* Rose (Metal Crafts Publishing Co.).

B. *Art Metal Work,* Payne (Manual Arts Press).

C. *Essentials of Metal Work,* Berg and Wing (Manual Arts Press).

QUESTIONS

1. Does art-metal work lend itself well to the principles of design? Explain (Ref. B, p. 42).

2. Should a project that is to have a high finish be laid out with a pencil or a scriber?

3. How many 45-deg. angles are there in a circle?

4. Give one object in combining natural metals to form another metal or alloy (Ref. C, p. 66).

5. Give three facts about the properties of aluminum (Ref. C, p. 71).

NECKTIE CLIP

This clip may be made of either nickel silver, brass, or copper. If the latter is used, it should be peened to harden it.

MATERIALS REQUIRED

18-ga. brass, nickel silver, or copper the size of the design.

DIRECTIONS

1. Select a design from this sheet or draw one of your own.

2. If you wish to transfer a design from this book to the metal, do so with carbon paper; if you make your own design, do so on squared paper.

3. Have the instructor approve the design.

4. Make out a bill of material.

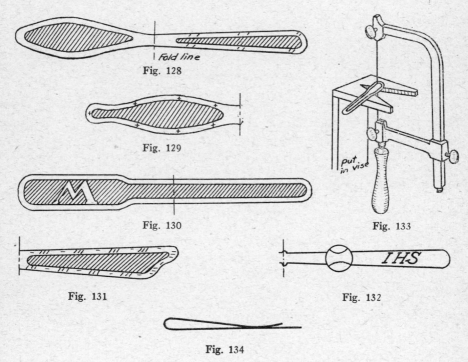

Fig. 128

Fig. 129

Fig. 130

Fig. 131

Fig. 132

Fig. 133

Fig. 134

5. Cut out the material according to the design.

6. Paste the design to the metal and allow it to dry.

7. On the pierced portion of the clip, center punch each sharp corner. All center-punch marks must be inside of the margin so that the entire hole will be in wasted or shaded portion.

8. Drill 1/16-in. hole at all of these locations.

9. Set up the saw and jig as shown in Figure 133, observing the following points:

a) The saw teeth must point toward the handle.
b) Clamp the blade in the end opposite the handle.
c) Put the blade through the hole in the work.
d) Tighten the end of the blade near the handle.

10. Saw out the waste portions observing the following rules:

a) Turn the curves slowly, sawing all the while.
b) Keep the blade tight.
c) Saw with slow regular strokes and avoid twisting the blade.

11. Saw around the outside of the clip in the same manner as you sawed the inside.
12. Smooth the sawed portions with a jewelers' file.
13. If there is any peening or chasing to do, do it now.
14. Buff the entire clip roughly.
15. Locate the bends which are shown at the dotted lines in the illustrations. They can be made with a small mallet over a thin piece of wrought iron. Be sure that it fits snugly over the tie.
16. Finally polish and then carefully buff the clip.
17. Lacquer it to preserve the finish.

REFERENCES

A. Brodhead-Garrett Catalogue.
B. *Metalcraft and Jewelry,* Kronquist (Manual Arts Press).
C. *Materials Handbook,* Brady (McGraw-Hill).
D. *Copper Work,* Rose (Metal Crafts Publishing Co.).
E. *Metal Work,* Jones (Bruce Publishing Co.).

QUESTIONS

1. What are the sizes of jewelers' saw blades? (Ref. A, p. 51.)
2. Which one of these blades is suitable for all-round work? (Ref. B, p. 20.)
3. Give some of the properties of nickel silver (Ref. C, p. 387).
4. Give the derivation of the word *copper*. Where have objects of copper been found? (Ref. D, p. 14.)
5. State ten ways to lay out metal (Ref. E, pp. 26–27).

BI- OR TRIMETAL LETTER OPENER

By combining copper, brass, and German silver in the design of these letter openers, a pleasing effect will result. Anyone of the three designs given below may be used, but it is much better to make a completely new design.

MATERIALS REQUIRED

18-ga. copper, brass, or German silver, the size determined by the design.

DIRECTIONS

1. Select a design either from this page or make one of your own. Additional designs may be found in *Metalcraft and Jewelry*, p. 129.

2. If you want to copy the design on this page, each type of metal must have a separate tracing. Figure 138 shows how the tracings appear on the metal.

3. Make out a bill of material with the sketch as a guide.

4. Cut the material to the proper size.

5. Cut out the paper design with a scissors.

6. Paste the designs to the pieces of metal.

7. Cut out the design on the metal, making the straight cuts with a tin snips, and the curved or difficult ones with a jewelers' saw.

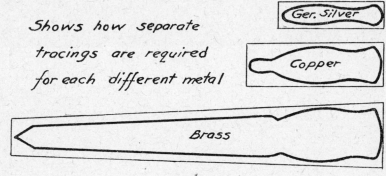

Shows how separate tracings are required for each different metal

Ger. Silver

Copper

Brass

Fig. 138

8. Smooth both sides with a jewelers' file until they are symmetrical.

9. Lay out the rivet holes shown in Figure 139. Check the locations.

10. Determine the drill size by checking the rivet in the drill gauge.

11. Before drilling clamp all of the pieces in a hand vise, center punch, and drill through all of them at the same time.

12. Rivet the pieces together. If there is any peening to be done, do so before riveting the pieces together.

13. Polish the opener on a buffer.

14. Give it a coat of clear lacquer.

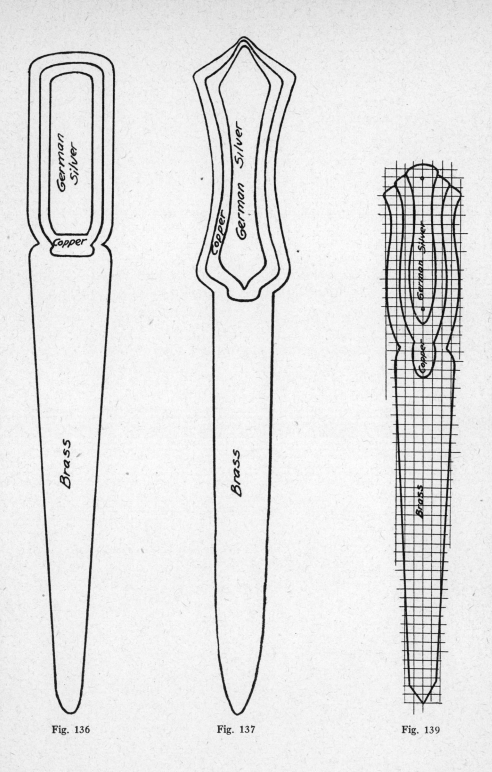

Fig. 136   Fig. 137   Fig. 139

REFERENCES

A. *Metalcraft and Jewelry,* Kronquist (Manual Arts Press).

B. *Metalwork Essentials,* Tustison and Kranzusch (Bruce Publishing Co.).

C. *Chemistry and Materials of Construction* (International Textbook Co.).

D. *Dictionary of Technical Terms,* Crispin (Bruce Publishing Co.).

E. *School and Home Workshop,* Schultz and Schultz (Allyn and Bacon).

QUESTIONS

1. What precautions must be observed in lacquering? (Ref. B, pp. 103–105.)

2. How much silver does German silver contain? What other metals does it contain?

3. Arrange two columns on a piece of paper. Call one "Alloys" and the other "Natural Metals." Then place the following metals in the correct column: iron, steel, copper, brass, bronze, tin, lead, zinc, German silver, aluminum, and pewter (Ref. B, pp. 152–171, Ref. C, and Ref. D).

4. What is the difference between an orthographic and an isometric drawing? (Ref. E, pp. 12 to 13.)

5. What is the meaning of the word *symmetrical?* (Ref. D.)

ROUND TRAY

This small tray, made from either copper or aluminum, can be used for a number of purposes. It makes a convenient tray for candy, but also may be used for pins, cards, or for an ash tray. The success of this job depends on the use of the raising hammer.

MATERIALS REQUIRED

1 piece, 5½ by 5½-in. 18- or 22-ga. sheet copper or 18-ga. aluminum.

DIRECTIONS

1. Make out a bill of material and have the instructor approve it.
2. Cut the material to size, that is, 5½ in. square.
3. If the tray is made of copper, it may be annealed by holding it in a flame until it reaches red heat and quenching it in cold water.

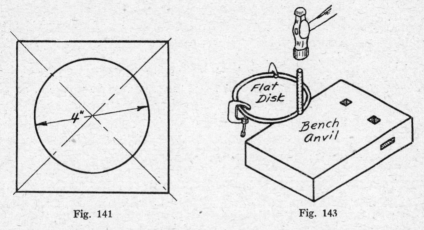

Fig. 141   Fig. 143

4. Locate the center of the stock by drawing the diagonals shown in Figure 141. With a dividers, draw a light circle 4 in. in diameter.
5. Secure a raising block of the correct shape.
6. The scribed circle of the tray must always be directly over the hole in the block. Guidelines should be marked around on the four sides of the block.
7. Start forming the copper to shape. Be careful of the following:

    a) Check the type of hammer with the instructor.
    b) Keep the edge of the tray flat with a mallet.
    c) Hit just inside of the edge of the tray only and always toward yourself with the hammer tipped at the angle shown in Figure 142.
    d) Work around the edge of the tray gradually. Do not drive it into position with only a few blows.
    e) As the copper hardens from the pounding, continue to anneal it as pointed out above.

8. When the tray is smooth and formed to shape as much as possible in the block, it can be deepened still more. Place it in an iron form and work it in the same manner. Check the form, hammer, and mallet with the instructor.

9. If you want to peen the tray, select the proper hammer and peen the inside holding it flat on an iron stake or anvil.

10. Reshape the bottom and use the form if necessary.

11. Set the dividers for the largest circle possible on the piece of metal. Find the center and scribe the circle. Cut it out and smooth it if necessary.

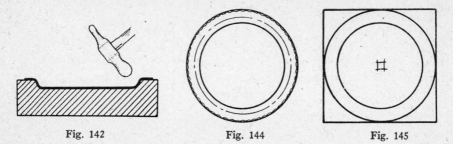

Fig. 142   Fig. 144   Fig. 145

12. Make the sheet-metal disk ¼ in. smaller in diameter than the tray and clamp it in position (Fig. 143). Place the tray on a flat stake or anvil.

13. Make the design around the edge of the tray with the correct punch (Fig. 143). Try the punching before you begin this operation.

14. Remove the disk and clamp the smaller one to it. It should fit about halfway on the rim as indicated (Fig. 144).

15. Secure the punch with the proper design from the instructor, and, as above, punch the design around this line.

16. If the tray is made of copper, clean it by dipping it in an acid solution. Keep it there until most of the black has been removed.

17. Clean off the remainder of the black oxide with steel wool and avoid finger marks.

18. If the job is to be polished, do it on a buffing wheel.

19. If the tray is made of copper it may be colored by dipping it in a liver of sulphur solution until the desired color is obtained. Rinse it with water and blot it dry.

20. Polish it lightly with a clean cloth and give it a coat of lacquer to preserve the finish.

REFERENCES

A. *Home Workshop Manual,* Wakeling (Popular Science Publishing Co.).

B. *101 Metal Working Projects,* Petersen (Bruce Publishing Co.).

C. *Art Metal Work,* Payne (Manual Arts Press).

D. *School and Home Workshop,* Schultz and Schultz (Allyn and Bacon).

E. *Essentials of Metalworking,* Berg and Wing (Manual Arts Press).

QUESTIONS

1. Tell how the various sheets of copper are designated (Ref. D, p. 192).
2. What is the property of metal that allows it to be readily formed into a tray or bowl? (Ref. E, p. 67.)
3. Hammering copper causes it to stiffen and become hard. How can this be eliminated? (Ref. C, p. 74.)
4. Tell how the black oxide that forms on copper which has been heated can be removed (Ref. C, p. 98).

OCTAGONAL TRAY

This octagonal tray may be made from either copper or aluminum. It is very effective as a table decoration. If it is carefully shaped, a well-rounded center will result.

MATERIALS REQUIRED

1 piece, 5½ by 5½-in. 18- or 22-ga. sheet copper or brass, or 18-ga. aluminum.

DIRECTIONS

1. Make out a bill of material and have the instructor approve it.
2. Cut the material to size, that is, 5½ in. square.

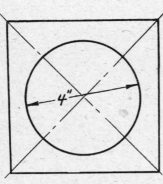

Fig. 146

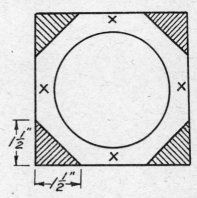

Fig. 147

3. If it is to be made of copper, anneal it by holding it in a flame until it reaches a red heat, and then quench it in cold water.
4. Locate the center of the stock by drawing diagonals with a pencil. Then with the dividers draw a light circle 4 in. in diameter (Fig. 146).
5. Secure a raising block of the right size.
6. The 4-in. circle must always be directly over the hole in the block. Make sure of this by making pencil marks around four sides of the block to serve as guide lines.
7. Start forming the copper, and be careful of the following:

    a) Check the kind of hammer with the instructor.
    b) Keep the edge of the tray flat with a mallet.
    c) Hit the edge of the tray only on the inside and toward you and at the angle shown in Figure 142.
    d) Work around the edge of the tray gradually. Do not try to drive it into place with only a few blows.
    e) As the work hardens through pounding, anneal it as directed above.

8. When the tray is smooth and formed to shape as far as possible in this block, it may be deepened still further.

9. Place it in an iron form and work it in the same way as before. Check the form, hammer, and mallet with the instructor.

10. Peen the inside of the tray with a hammer producing the size marks that you want.

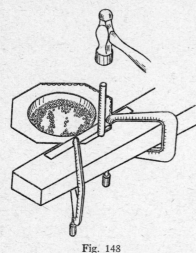

Fig. 148

11. If necessary, reshape the bottom on a form or with a mallet.

12. The tray should now appear as shown in Figure 147. The four sides marked by an X should be equal in size as well as straight.

13. Measure all of the corners as shown in Figure 147 and draw the four lines.

14. Cut off the corners after the instructor has checked them.

15. Clamp a straight piece of heavy-gauge sheet metal about the length shown in Figure 148 to one edge of the work. It should be 3/32 in. from the edge.

16. Get the correct punch from the instructor and make the design around the edge of the tray (Fig. 148).

17. Secure a disk of the correct size from the instructor and clamp it in position on the tray. The tray should overhang the edge of the flat anvil (Fig. 143).

18. Punch the design into the overhang.

19. Clean the tray by dipping it into an acid solution until most of the dirt has been removed.

20. Clean the remainder of the dirt with steel wool; avoid fingerprints.

21. If the tray is to be polished, do it on a buffing wheel.

22. If the tray is made of copper it may be colored by placing it in a liver of sulphur solution until the desired color is obtained. Rinse it with water and blot it dry.

23. Polish it lightly with a clean cloth and give it a coat of lacquer to preserve the finish.

REFERENCES

A. *The Home Workshop Manual,* Wakeling (Popular Science Publishing Co.).

B. *Sheet Metal Workers Manual,* Broemel (Frederick Drake and Co.).

C. *Metal Work,* Jones (Bruce Publishing Co.).

QUESTIONS

1. How should an object to be polished be held against the buffing wheel? (Ref. A, p. 207.)

2. Can aluminum be soldered readily? Why? (Ref. B, p. 453.)

3. Name three ores from which aluminum is obtained (Ref. B, p. 452).

4. State the relation, if any, between a circle and a semicircle (Ref. B, p. 485).

5. Should a decoration fit in with the design of the contents of a room? Explain (Ref. C, p. 46).

CHASED BRACELET

This is another type of bracelet. Instead of the design being etched, it is chased. This type of ornamentation, although more difficult to accomplish, is considered to be better looking. The designs given here are but a few of the possible ones for this style of bracelet.

MATERIALS REQUIRED

1 piece, 18-ga. copper, brass, or German silver the size of the design.

DIRECTIONS

1. Decide on the design to be used, and then draw it on a piece of squared paper observing the following rules:

   a) The length of the bracelet may be determined by winding a narrow strip of paper around the wrist for which it is intended. The ends should be ½ in. apart.

   b) The design should lend itself to chasing, that is, it should not be too complicated.

   c) It is preferable to make your own design, however, suggestions may be obtained from the instructor or the references.

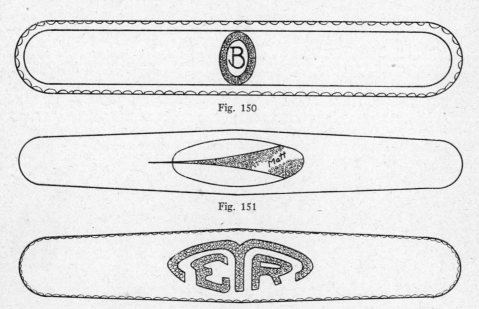

Fig. 150

Fig. 151

Fig. 152

2. After the instructor checks the design, cut the metal.

3. If the ends are to be rounded, set the dividers at half the width of the bracelet and scribe a semicircle at each end.

4. Cut the bracelet to shape and file the edges smooth.

5. Transfer the design to the metal.

6. If another type of ornamentation is to be used beside chasing, such as peening, do this now if possible.

7. Clamp a piece of narrow heavy-gauge metal to the line to be chased (Fig. 153). Clamp both pieces to the stake. Chase all of the straight lines first, but before doing so practice on a piece of scrap metal.

8. If the design possesses any lettering or other irregularities, chase these portions first.

9. Bend the bracelet to fit the wrist. Make a slight bend first, and end up with the sharper curved ends (Fig. 93).

10. If the bracelet is to be polished, do so on a buffer.

11. If the bracelet is made of copper, it may be colored by dipping it in a liver of sulphur solution, until the desired color is obtained. Rinse it with water and blot it dry.

12. Polish it lightly with a clean cloth and give it a coat of lacquer to preserve the finish.

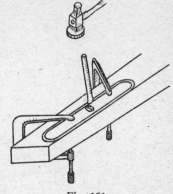

Fig. 153

REFERENCES

A. *School and Home Workshop,* Schultz and Schultz (Allyn and Bacon).

B. *Metal Work,* Jones (Bruce Publishing Co.).

C. *Cold Metal Working,* Van Leuven (McGraw-Hill).

QUESTIONS

1. To what distance should the dividers be set to get a half circle at the end of a bracelet 1¼ in. wide? (Ref. A, p. 192.)

2. Why are copper cooking utensils frequently lined with tin? (Ref. A, p. 192.)

3. Tell what corrosion is in regard to copper (Ref. B, p. 50).

4. What is meant by the statement, "Drawing and design is older than written language"? (Ref. A, p. 6.)

5. Give the melting points of copper, aluminum, tin, and lead. Which is the highest? Lowest? (Ref. C, p. 266.)

NAPKIN CLIP

A set of these animal-shaped clips for small napkins would look very well placed around the dinner table, especially if they are made of polished copper or brass.

MATERIALS REQUIRED

1 piece, 22-ga. brass or copper the size of the design.

DIRECTIONS

1. Make out a bill of material and have the instructor approve it.
2. Make a design on squared paper (Figs. 155–161). If you have an original design of your own, it is much better to use it than to copy one of the designs given here.

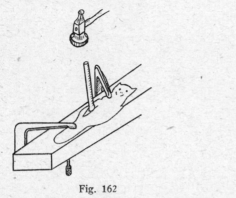

Fig. 162

Fig. 163

3. After the instructor has checked the design, cut out the metal.
4. Paste the design to the metal.
5. Cut out as much of the clip as you can with a tin snips, and for the remainder use a jewelers' saw and a jig cutting just outside of the line (see Fig. 133).
6. Smooth the outline with jewelers' files.
7. Clamp the work to a flat stake for chasing (Fig. 162). The instructor will show you this operation. It is best to practice on a piece of scrap before starting.
8. Chase the design on the surface of the work, holding the tool as shown in Figure 162.
9. Bend the flap around a piece of 1 by $\frac{1}{8}$-in. wrought iron as shown in Figure 163.
10. Clean the job with steel wool, being sure to avoid fingerprints.
11. If the job is to be polished, do so on a buffer. If it is made of copper it may be colored by dipping it in a liver of sulphur solution until the desired color is obtained. Rinse it in water and blot it dry.
12. Polish it lightly with a clean cloth and then give it a coat of lacquer to preserve the finish.

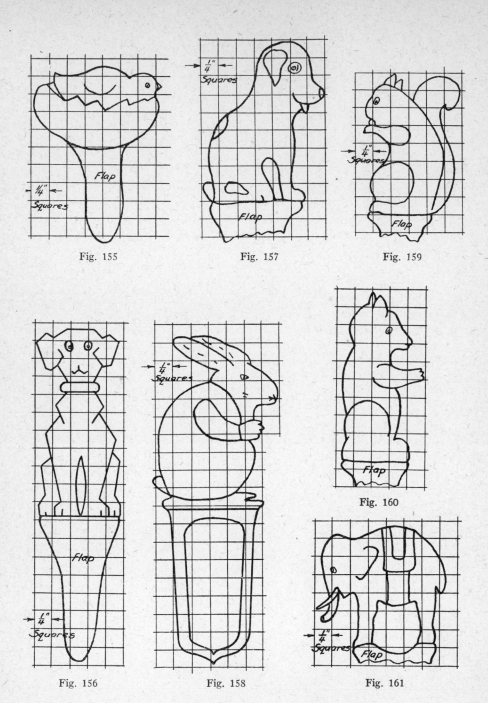

Fig. 155

Fig. 157

Fig. 159

Fig. 156

Fig. 158

Fig. 160

Fig. 161

REFERENCES

A. *Metal Work,* Jones (Bruce Publishing Co.).

B. *School and Home Shop Work,* Schultz and Schultz (Allyn and Bacon).

C. *Essentials of Metal Working,* Berg and Wing (Manual Arts Press).

D. *Art Metal Work,* Payne (Manual Arts Press).

QUESTIONS

1. In transferring design to art metal, do you like to use carbon paper or paste the design to the metal? Why?

2. Rouge is an abrasive put on a buffing wheel. Explain (Ref. A, p. 50).

3. Is brass an alloy? Of what metals? (Ref. B, p. 193.)

4. Of what metals is the alloy babbit made? (Ref. C, p. 75.)

5. Give three examples telling how we know that the ancients used copper (Ref. D, p. 14).

BELT CLIP

Have you a knife, keys, or perhaps a whistle that may be easily lost? This belt clip will insure their safety. Many more designs are possible than the one shown in Figure 165.

MATERIALS REQUIRED

1 piece, ¾ by 4-in. 18-ga. copper.
1 cotter key, ⅛ by 1¾ in.

DIRECTIONS

1. Make the design for the front of the belt hook on squared paper.
2. Have the instructor check the design and then cut the metal to size.
3. Scribe the outline of the belt hook, using the pattern.
4. Trim off the ends and file them to shape. Get the fine files from the instructor.

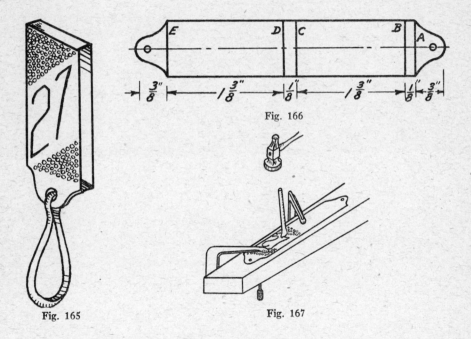

Fig. 166

Fig. 165   Fig. 167

5. With a scriber, draw lines *A, B, C, D,* and *E* shown in Figure 166.
6. Transfer the design to the metal.
7. Get a peen punch from the instructor. Clamp the clip on a stake and peen it with a medium machinist's hammer (Fig. 167).
8. Keep the work clamped to the stake and do the chasing (Fig. 167). Before chasing it is best to practice on a piece of scrap metal.
9. Layout the holes, 3/16 in. from each end (Fig. 166) and center punch them. Make the holes with a 3/16-in. drill.

10. Make the bends carefully in the following order:

a) The first bend is a right-angle bend made by clamping the clip to the stake (Fig. 168).

b) The second bend is made by clamping it flat to a stake with a bar of metal over it. Bend it down to shape by holding a piece of wrought iron, ¾ by ⅛ in., against the bend and hammering it carefully into shape (Fig. 169).

c) The third bend is made by clamping a piece of wrought iron, ⅛ by 1 in., in place and bending the clip around it. Make sure that the holes come together.

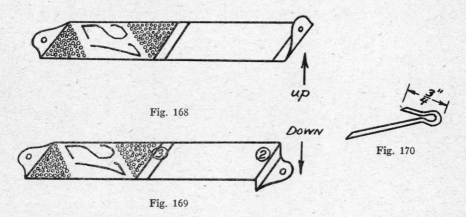

Fig. 168

up

Down

Fig. 169

Fig. 170

11. Cut off the short end of a ⅛ by 1¾-in. cotter key, ¾ in. from the top (Fig. 170).

12. File the ends so that they will meet flush (Fig. 170).

13. Place the key into position in the clip.

14. Bend the key round with a small needle-nose pliers or around a small stake. The ends must meet as shown in Figure 165.

15. Clean the clip well with steel wool, and avoid fingerprints.

16. If the clip is to be polished, use a buffer. If it is made of copper, it may be colored by dipping it in a liver of sulphur solution until it is black, after which it should be rinsed with water and blotted dry.

17. Polish it lightly with a damp cloth dusted with pumice stone. Rub off the black so that the copper shows in spots.

18. Rewash the clip and dry it.

19. Lacquer the clip to preserve the finish.

REFERENCES

A. *School and Home Shopwork,* Schultz and Schultz (Allyn and Bacon).
B. *Metal Work,* Jones (Bruce Publishing Co.).
C. *Essentials of Metal Work,* Berg and Wing (Manual Arts Press).
D. *Art Metal Work,* Payne (Manual Arts Press).

QUESTIONS

1. Describe the common method for transporting copper from Duluth to Cleveland.

2. Bronze was used by the ancients. How did they make it? (Ref. A, p. 193.)

3. Discuss briefly the uses of copper (Ref. B, p. 54).

4. Give three facts in regard to nickel (Ref. C, p. 72).

5. Give some advantages that art-metal work as a craft possesses and that some of the other crafts lack (Ref. D, p. 10).

SQUARE MATCHBOX HOLDER

Although small in size, this matchbox holder requires considerable skill to make. It makes a very nice table piece because its copper hues blend in with most furniture.

MATERIALS REQUIRED

Top — 1 piece, 2¼ by 3½-in., 18-ga. copper.

Bottom — 1 piece, 2 3/16 by 2¼-in., 18-ga. copper.

DIRECTIONS

1. Make out a bill of material and have the instructor approve it.

2. Cut out the material as specified.

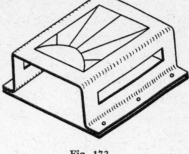

Fig. 172

3. Draw the lines on the larger piece of copper as shown in Figure 173 in the following order: center lines, A, B, C, and D. Use a sharp pointed pencil, because a scriber will scratch the copper.

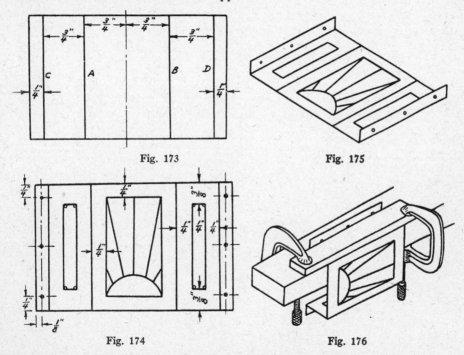

Fig. 173

Fig. 175

Fig. 174

Fig. 176

4. Draw the lines for the slot through which the matches will be struck (Fig. 174).

5. Drill the 1/16-in. holes for the saw piercing, 1/16 in. from each corner. Be sure that they are in the waste portion of the work.

6. Saw out the slots with a jewelers' saw (Fig. 133).

7. File the slots with small files until they are rectangular.

8. Locate the rivet holes shown in Figure 174.

9. After making light punch marks, drill the holes with a No. 42 drill.

10. Draw the design on the metal with a pencil (Fig. 174).

11. Chase the design. To guide the work, clamp a straight piece of sheet metal on the line that you are chasing (Fig. 148).

12. Bend the top to shape with a light rawhide mallet and finish the bends, if necessary, with a light machinists' hammer (Figs. 175 and 176).

    a) Make the bends shown in Figure 175. Clamp the holder so that the line is at the edge of the stake and do the bending in the direction of the design.

    b) Make the last two bends. To avoid bending the metal at the slots, clamp a ¾-in. bar of metal over them (Fig. 176).

    c) Square up the form and try the matchbox in place.

13. Fit the top to the bottom and carefully mark the holes on each side.

14. Make light punch marks and drill the end holes with a No. 42 drill. File off the burrs.

15. Secure 3/32 by ¼-in. roundhead, copper rivets, and after checking them with the instructor, cut them off, and do the riveting. The instructor will show you how to work a special rivet set.

16. Drill the remaining holes and complete the riveting.

17. Clean the entire matchbox with steel wool, holding it with a paper towel to avoid finger marks.

18. Place it in a liver of sulphur solution until the desired color is obtained. Rinse it in water and place it in a sawdust barrel to dry.

19. With a small damp cloth sprinkled lightly with pumice stone, rub the sun design until it shines, together with a few spots on the sides.

20. Wash off the pumice stone and blot the holder dry.

21. Give the holder a coat of lacquer to preserve the finish.

REFERENCES

    A. *Essentials of Metal Working,* Berg and Wing (Manual Arts Press).

    B. *Metal Work,* Jones (Bruce Publishing Co.).

QUESTIONS

    1. Give several uses of brass (Ref. A, p. 74).

    2. How and when is the behavior of copper different from steel? (Ref. A, p. 71.)

    3. Tell why it is advisable whenever possible to use a metal guide during the chasing operation.

    4. What is a "pickle" and how is it used in connection with copper work? (Ref. B, p. 50.)

    5. Rivets used in the making of small boats are frequently made of copper. Why is this metal used? (Ref. B, p. 54).

SECTION III

ORNAMENTAL IRON PROJECTS

SMALL RIVETED VASE STAND

Although the instructions are for the particular vase shown, they can be adapted to a vase of almost any shape.

MATERIALS REQUIRED

Legs — 2 pieces, 1/16 by ¼ by 4¼-in. round edge, flat, cold-rolled wire.

Vase holders — 2 pieces, 1/16 by ¼ by 9¼-in. round edge, flat, cold-rolled wire.

DIRECTIONS

1. Before starting, secure the vase for which you desire a holder. Check it with the instructor as to the desirable shape.

2. Make out a bill of material and have the instructor approve it.

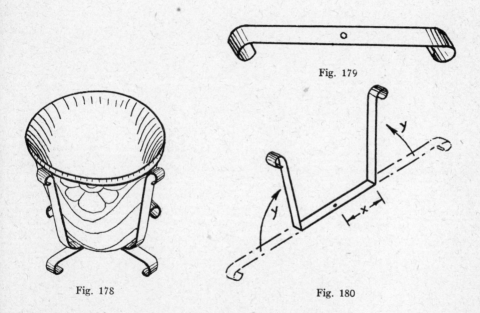

Fig. 179

Fig. 178

Fig. 180

3. Cut out the stock as listed in the bill of material.

4. File the ends square on all pieces.

5. Drill a No. 41 hole in the center of all the pieces.

6. Form the loop shown in Figure 179 on both ends of all pieces, using a rod 5/16 in. in diameter.

7. Bend the sections Y in the direction shown in Figure 180. Be sure that the loops point outward.

8. Rivet all of the pieces together with a No. 12 brad or 3/32 cold-rolled stock.

9. Clean off the loose black scale and give the job a coat of flat black enamel.

REFERENCES

A. *Dictionary of Technical Terms,* Crispin (Bruce Publishing Co.).
B. *Materials of Industry,* Mersereau (McGraw-Hill).
C. *Elementary Wrought Iron,* Bollinger (Bruce Publishing Co.).

QUESTIONS

1. What is meant by the word *jig?* (Ref. A.)
2. What are some of the characteristics of wrought iron? (Ref. B, p. 401.)
3. How far should a rivet project beyond the pieces being riveted? (Ref. C, p. 38.)
4. Explain briefly four different finishes possible on wrought iron (Ref. C, pp. 47–49).

SMALL VASE STAND

While these instructions show how the vase stand in Figure 182 is made, this holder can be adapted to any particular vase.

MATERIALS REQUIRED

Legs — 2 pieces, 1/16 by ¼ by 4¼-in. round edge, flat, cold-rolled wire.

Vase holder — 1 piece, 1/16 by ¼ by 9¼-in. round edge, flat, cold-rolled wire.

Handle — 1 piece, 1/16 by ¼ by 12-in. round edge, flat, cold-rolled wire.

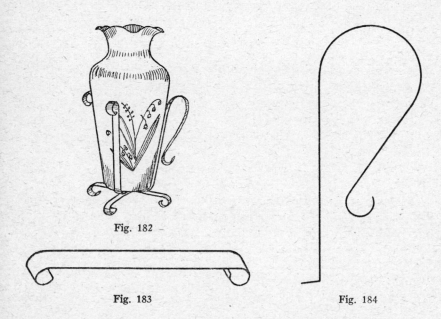

Fig. 182

Fig. 183

Fig. 184

DIRECTIONS

1. After the vase has been selected for which the holder is to be made, make out a bill of material and have the instructor approve it.

2. Cut out the stock as listed in the bill of material.

3. File the ends square on all the pieces.

4. Form the loops shown in Figure 183 over a rod 5/16 in. in diameter on both ends of all the pieces. On the handle piece the loops should be turned in the opposite direction; on the other pieces in the same direction.

5. Use Figure 184 as a guide in bending the handle. Be sure to keep the long pieces the same length.

6. On the long pieces, measure off the distance X, which is equal to one half the diameter of the vase (Fig. 185).

7. Bend the sections Y in the directions shown; be sure that the loops point outward.

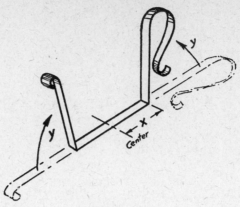

Fig. 185

8. Measure the middle of the center of the pieces so that they can be held in place while welding.

9. Before welding check with the instructor. Weld the holder and the legs separately, and then to each other.

10. Clean off the loose black scale and give the stand a coat of flat black enamel.

REFERENCES

A. *Dictionary of Technical Terms*, Crispin (Bruce Publishing Co.).

B. *Materials of Industry*, Mersereau (McGraw-Hill).

C. *Elementary Wrought Iron*, Bollinger (Bruce Publishing Co.).

QUESTIONS

1. What is meant by the word *jig?* (Ref. A.)

2. What are some of the characteristics of wrought iron? (Ref. B, p. 401.)

3. How far should a rivet project beyond the pieces being riveted? (Ref. C, p. 38.)

4. Explain briefly four different kinds of finishes possible on wrought iron (Ref. C, pp. 47 to 49).

SIMPLE SHOE SCRAPER

This shoe scraper is a handy little device that can be mounted on the steps and used to remove mud and snow from your shoes.

MATERIALS REQUIRED

Scraper — 1 piece, ⅛ by ¾ by 6-in. wrought iron.

Legs — 2 pieces, ⅛ by ¾ by 3½-in. wrought iron.

DIRECTIONS

1. Make out a bill of material and have the instructor approve it.

2. Cut out the materials as listed in the bill of material.

3. File all of the ends square.

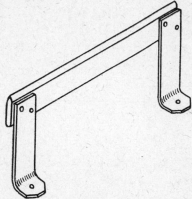

Fig. 188

Legs

4. Lay out the legs as shown in Figure 189 and draw the lines in the following order: *A, B,* and *C.*

5. Lay out the holes shown in Figure 190. Draw the diagonals first, and then measure off the holes *D* and *E.*

6. Drill the holes marked *D*, 3/16 in., and the ones marked *E*, ⅛ in. File off the burrs.

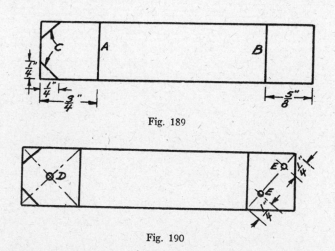

Fig. 189

Fig. 190

7. Cut off the diagonals *C* with a hack saw (Fig. 189) and file them smooth.

8. With a vise and hammer, bend along line *A*, Figure 191. Be sure to check these bends with a square.

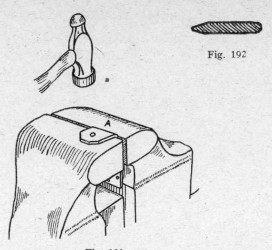

Fig. 192

Fig. 191

Scraper

9. Shape the scraping edge with a coarse file (Fig. 192).

10. Take one leg at a time and hold it in position on the scraper. Mark off the upper end only of each leg.

11. Center punch and drill the upper hole on each side with a ⅛-in. drill.

12. Rivet each leg in place on the scraper through the top hole with ⅛-in. roundhead rivets.

13. Square up the legs if necessary using a square.

14. Using the unriveted holes in the legs as a guide, drill the holes in the scraper.

15. Rivet the last two holes with the same size rivets used above.

16. Remove the loose black scale with emery cloth.

17. It is recommended that the scraper be finished with black enamel.

REFERENCES

A. *Dictionary of Technical Terms*, Crispin (Bruce Publishing Co.).

B. *Metal Work*, Jones (Bruce Publishing Co.).

C. *School and Home Shopwork*, Schultz and Schultz (Allyn and Bacon).

QUESTIONS

1. Give the meaning of these words: *diagonal* and *intersection* (Ref. A).

2. Look up the price of a 12-oz. ball-peen hammer in a shop catalogue.

3. Give an important caution to be observed in drilling (Ref. B, p. 36).

4. What is meant when it is said that the hardness of steel depends upon the carbon present? (Ref. C, p. 173.)

5. Discuss tools as used by the ancients. Answer this orally for the instructor (Ref. C, p. 172).

DOOR HOLDER

If you have a door that won't stay open, this door holder will remedy the situation.

MATERIALS REQUIRED

Circular section — 1 piece, 1/16 by ½ by 7-in. wrought iron.
Clip — 1 piece, 1/16 by ½ by 8-in. wrought iron.

DIRECTIONS

1. Make out a bill of material and have the instructor approve it.
2. Cut the material to size as listed in the bill of material.

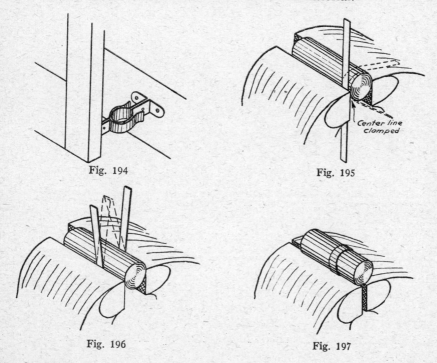

Fig. 194

Fig. 195

Center line clamped

Fig. 196

Fig. 197

Circular Section

3. Find and mark the center of this piece.
4. Insert it into a vise with the center line touching the ¾-in. diameter rod (Fig. 195).
5. Bend the piece as far as possible over the rod (Fig. 195) with the fingers, or use a hammer if necessary.
6. Then clamp the piece as shown in Figure 196 and bend the ends together so that the tips touch.
7. Reverse the bar and the piece as shown in Figure 197, and while forcing them down with the hand close the vise jaws. It should now look like Figure 198.

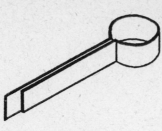

Fig. 198

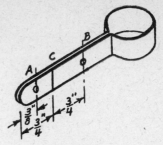

Fig. 199

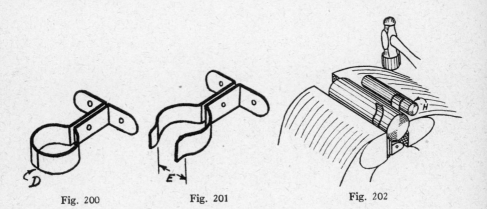

Fig. 200   Fig. 201   Fig. 202

8. If the ends are uneven cut off the longer one. Round them off with a grinder or a file (Figs. 198 and 199).

9. Lay out holes A and B and also the fold mark C in Figure 199.

10. Drill hole A 3/16 in. and B ⅛ in. in diameter.

11. Rivet the double piece together at B in Figure 199.

12. Spring the ends apart gradually, forming the right angles shown in Figure 200.

Clip

13. Bend the metal for the clip around a bar ⅞ in. in diameter, repeating directions 3–12 above.

14. Split the center with a hack saw as shown at D in Figure 200.

15. With a pliers and a bending jig, form the clip (Fig. 201). The space E must be set so that it will clip the other piece. If necessary form the clip in a vise (Fig. 202). The smaller bar (at H in Fig. 202) can be held in place while the ends are being hammered.

16. Round off the clip ends slightly with a file or on a grinder.

17. The holder may now be finished as desired.

REFERENCES

A. *Elementary Wrought Iron,* Bollinger (Bruce Publishing Co.).

B. *School and Home Workshop,* Schultz and Schultz (Allyn and Bacon).

QUESTIONS

1. Make a safety rule of your own for the operation of a squaring shears.
2. How is cast iron formed? (Ref. B, p. 175.)
3. What is meant by good workmanship? (Ref. B, p. 37.)
4. How are rivets removed? (Ref. A, p. 38.)
5. Are rivets made of soft iron? Why? (Ref. A, p. 38.)

DISH STAND

This stand is an excellent holder for flowerpots, trays, and bowls, especially if it is finished in color and sprayed lightly with a bronzing powder. The size can be altered to fit any size pot or bowl.

MATERIALS REQUIRED

Legs — 3 pieces, ⅛ by ½ by 8¼-in. wrought iron.

Loop — 1 piece, ⅛ by ½-in. wrought iron (the length is equal the circumference of the circle, the diameter of which should be measured on the bowl; a good average is 5 in.).

DIRECTIONS

1. Make out a bill of material after having determined the length of the loop, and then have the instructor approve it.

2. Cut out the stock as listed and file all the ends square.

Loop

3. Lay out the holes shown in Figure 205; first the ones marked *A*, and then the one at *B* in the center, and finally the ones marked *C*, 1/3 of the loop from hole *B*. The latter may be found with a dividers.

Fig. 204

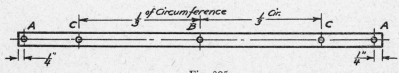

Fig. 205

4. Center punch the hole locations, and bore them with a ⅛-in. drill. File off the burrs.

5. Round the loop with the extreme left end of a form roller until the ends close.

6. Cut a piece of No. 22 black iron, ⅜ by 1 in.

7. Place it on the inside of the loop under the end holes and mark their locations.

8. Bore them with a ⅛-in. drill and file off the burrs.

9. Rivet the piece in place inside the loop and keep the ends closed. Use ⅛-in. roundhead rivets with the heads on the outside.

Legs

10. Round one end of each leg as shown in Figure 206 on a power grinder.

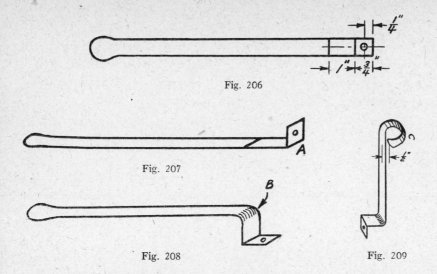

Fig. 206

Fig. 207

Fig. 208

Fig. 209

11. Heat these ends red hot and flatten them slightly with a machinists' hammer on an anvil.

12. Lay out the holes at the other ends of the legs, center punch, and make them with a ⅛-in. drill.

13. Lay out the fold marks shown in Figure 206.

14. Make the sharp folds shown at *A* in Figure 207 in a vise with a hammer.

15. Make the slightly round fold shown at *B* in Figure 208.

16. Make the bends shown at *C* in Figure 209.

17. Rivet the legs to the loop using ⅛ by ½-in. roundhead rivets with the heads on the outside.

18. Check the stand to make sure that it stands straight.

19. Clean off the loose black oxide with emery cloth.

20. Finish it as desired.

REFERENCES

A. *Metal Work,* Jones (Bruce Publishing Co.).

B. *Essentials of Metal Working,* Berg and Wing (Manual Arts Press).

QUESTIONS

1. What is a milling machine and for what is it used? (Ref. B, pp. 140, 141.)

2. Wrought iron melted in a crucible with charcoal, adds carbon and makes . . . . (Ref. B, p. 149).

3. What is a crucible? (Ref. B, p. 94.)

4. Give three uses for a dividers (Ref. B, p. 17).

5. Give two factors that regulate the speed of a drill (Ref. B, p. 42).

FLOWERPOT BRACKET

By varying the diameter of the pot holder, this wall bracket can be built to fit any particular flowerpot or vase.

MATERIALS REQUIRED

Ornaments — 2 pieces, 1/16 by ⅜ by 9½-in. wrought iron.

Holder — 1 piece, 1/16 by ⅜ by 10½ in. plus the circumference of the pot you desire to place in this holder.

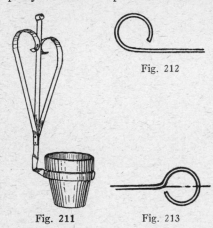

Fig. 212

Fig. 211   Fig. 213

DIRECTIONS

1. Make out a bill of material and have the instructor approve it.
2. Cut out the materials as listed above and file the ends of all pieces square.

Holder

3. Form one end of the longer piece around a bar 5/16 in. in diameter (Fig. 212, and *Metalwork Essentials*, Tustison and Kranzusch, Bruce Publishing Co., p. 122).

4. Form the loop so that the center lines up with the metal (Fig. 213, and the reference in 3 above).

5. On the extreme left end of the form roller, shape the opposite end to fit the flowerpot (Fig. 212).

6. Bend it to the shape shown in Figure 213 with the vise and the fingers.

7. The piece should now look like Figure 214. At a point 1 in. from the large loop, make a 90-deg. bend (Fig. 214).

8. Check over Figure 167 in *Metalwork Essentials*, by Tustison and Kranzusch, p. 115. Then place the piece in a high sheet-metal vise with the loop away from you. With an adjustable open-end wrench placed as close to your previous bend as possible, make a quarter turn as shown at *A* in Figures 215 and 216.

9. Keep the first wrench in place and set another one of the same type as close to the loop as possible. Holding the first wrench steady, raise the second wrench up giving the loop a quarter turn (Figs. 216 and 217).

Ornaments

10. File off all of the sharp corners on both pieces.

11. Form both pieces in a bending jig as shown in Figure 218.

12. Locate the holes marked *X* by laying the pieces on a flat surface (Fig. 218). Check each piece with each other to see that the holes match.

13. Make the holes with a ⅛-in. drill.

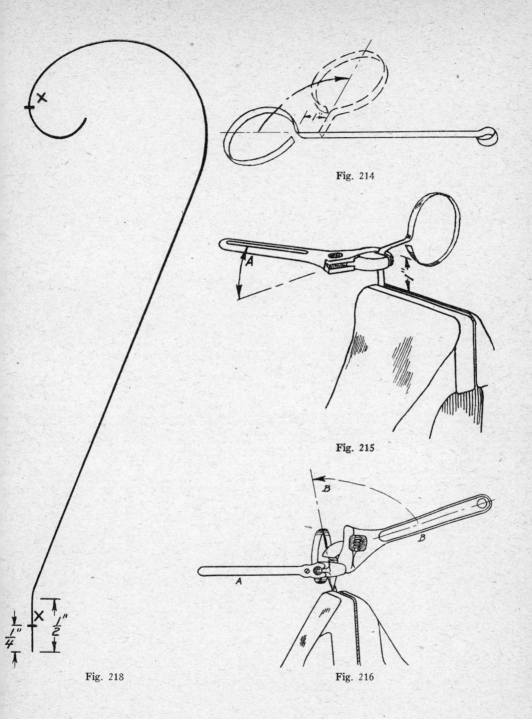

Fig. 214

Fig. 215

Fig. 218

Fig. 216

Assembly

14. Locate the holes in upright piece by holding the ornaments in the desired position and then marking them.

15. Make the holes with a ⅛-in. drill.

16. After reading the following directions, fasten the pieces together with ⅛-in. roundhead rivets.

a) Do not allow too much of the rivet to project.

b) Rivet the bottom in position first.

c) The top rivet will be difficult to flatten. It is necessary to hold the head on a small round stake and flatten it with the open end of a small ball-peen hammer.

17. Clean off the loose black scale.

18. The holder may be finished as desired, but flat black enamel is recommended.

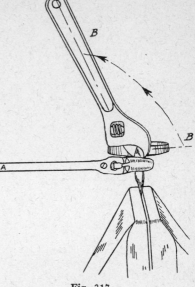

Fig. 217

REFERENCES

A. *Metalwork Essentials,* Tustison and Kranzusch (Bruce Publishing Co.).

B. *Cold Metal Working,* Van Leuven (McGraw-Hill).

QUESTIONS

1. What part of a turn is 120 deg.?

2. In a simple drawing give your idea of a scroll.

3. State three precautions in the use of a hand hack saw (Ref. A, Unit 16; Ref. B, p. 31).

4. With a simple sketch illustrate the relationships between the following parts of a file: point, cutting face, heel, and tang (Ref. A, p. 87).

5. Give three characteristics of wrought iron (Ref. B, p. 224).

METER BOARD CANDLESTICK

Have you ever had to change a fuse in the dark? Usually your fingers have been burned trying to get enough light from matches. This emergency light, fastened to the board and supplied with a candle and matches, is just what you need.

MATERIALS REQUIRED

Candleholder — 1 piece, 1 by 2½-in. IX tin plate.
Disk — 1 piece, 3 by 3-in. IX tin plate.
Base — 1 piece, 1/16 by ½ by 9⅜-in. wrought iron.
Matchbox holder — 1/16 by ½ by 4⅝-in. wrought iron.

DIRECTIONS

1. Make out a bill of material and have the instructor approve it.
2. Cut out the stock as listed.

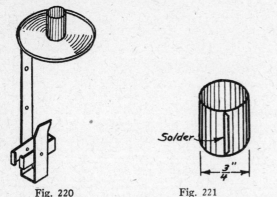

Fig. 220

Solder

Fig. 221

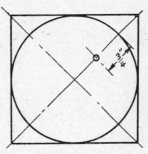

Fig. 222

Candleholder

3. Form the cylinder shown in Figure 221. The ends should overlap ⅛ in. for soldering.
4. Solder the candleholder along the seam.

Fig. 223

Disk

5. Locate the center of the square piece of material and scribe a 3-in. circle on it with the dividers.
6. Carefully cut out the circle with a tinner's snips and file off the burrs.

7. Locate the hole shown in Figure 222. Starting with a prick punch, make the hole with a No. 9 solid punch.

8. Turn a 3/32-in. burr around the edge (Fig. 220).

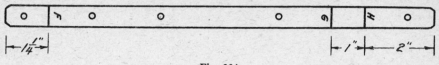

Fig. 224

Base

9. File off all of the corners about 1/16 in. (Fig. 223.)

10. Lay out holes *A, B, C, D,* and *E* in order shown in Figure 223 and center punch the locations.

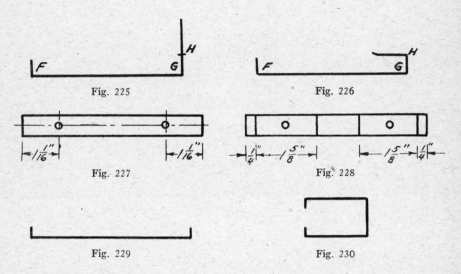

Fig. 225   Fig. 226

Fig. 227   Fig. 228

Fig. 229   Fig. 230

11. On a power drill press make the ⅛-in. holes at these locations.

12. Lay out the fold marks with a scriber in the following order: *F, G, H* (Fig. 224).

13. Make the bends *F* and *G* shown in Figure 225 with a vise and hammer.

14. Make the bend *H* in Figure 226 with a stake and hammer.

15. Bend the end slightly upward as shown in Figure 226.

Match Holder

16. Locate the holes shown in Figure 227, center punch, bore them with a ⅛-in. drill, and file off the burrs.

17. Locate the fold marks shown in Figure 228.

18. Make the end folds (Fig. 229) with a vise and hammer.

19. Make the inside folds (Fig. 230) with a stake and hammer. Be sure that it fits the matchbox.

Assembly

20. Solder the candleholder to the disk.
21. Rivet the matchbox holder to the base with the flatheads of the rivets on the inside. Do the riveting on a stake of the proper size.
22. Rivet the candleholder to the base.
23. Remove the black oxide with emery cloth.
24. Finish the holder as desired.

REFERENCES

A. *Metal Work*, Jones (Bruce Publishing Co.).
B. *Essentials of Metal Work*, Berg and Wing (Manual Arts Press).
C. *School and Home Shop Work*, Schultz and Schultz (Allyn and Bacon).

QUESTIONS

1. For what is the rivet set or snap used? (Ref. A, p. 32.)
2. What is wrought iron? (Ref. B, p. 83.)
3. Why does a craftsman take good care of his tools? (Ref. C, p. 175.)
4. Give a few characteristics of wrought iron (Ref. B; p. 84).
5. Explain what you understand by machine forging (Ref. B, p. 108).

TEAPOT STAND

This easily made, useful little stand will make a welcome gift anywhere.

MATERIALS REQUIRED

Base — 1 piece, ½ in. wider and longer than the tile, 22-ga. black sheet iron.

Legs — 1 piece, ⅛ by ½ by 11-in. wrought iron.

Tile — 1 piece, approximately 4¼ by 4¼-in. bathroom wall tile.

DIRECTIONS

1. Secure the tile, make out a bill of material, and have the instructor approve it.

2. Cut out the materials as listed above.

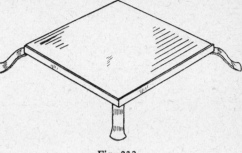

Fig. 232

Base

3. With a combination square and scriber, lay out a ¼-in. margin around the piece and draw the diagonals shown in Figure 233.

4. Lay out and center punch the holes shown in Figure 233.

5. Bore the holes with a No. 34 drill.

6. Cut out the little squares at each corner of the base with the tip of a tinner's snips.

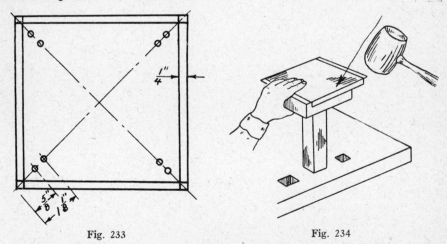

Fig. 233

Fig. 234

7. Go over the entire piece carefully with a file and emery cloth to remove all of the scale and the burred edges.

8. With a bar folder set at ¼ in., fold two opposite sides at 90 deg.

9. Then fold the other two sides as far as possible on the bar folder.

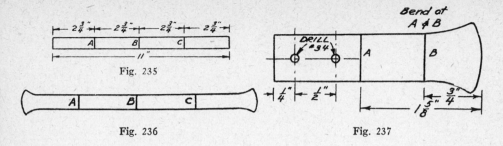

Fig. 235

Fig. 236

Fig. 237

10. Then with a square stake and mallet (Fig. 234), bend all of the sides until they are at right angles to the base and until the corners fit together snugly. Keep adjusting the sides until the tile fits.

Legs

11. Lay out the legs as shown in Figure 235.

12. Hammer each end of the legpiece until it resembles Figure 236. The instructor will show you how to do it. Cut them off at *A* and *C* with a hack saw.

13. Repeat the last operation on the remainder of the piece and cut it apart at *B*. This should result in four almost identical pieces.

14. Lay out the lines and the holes on each piece as shown in Figure 237 and make the holes with a No. 34 drill.

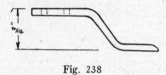

Fig. 238

15. Clean each piece thoroughly with emery cloth and remove the burred edges with a file.

16. Peen each piece lightly with the round end of a machinists' hammer to within 1 in. of the shaped end.

17. Hammer each piece to shape using the copper jaws of a vise.

18. Assemble the stand with 1-lb. tinner's rivets inserted from the inside. Rivet it firmly and carefully.

19. Apply an oxidized finish to the entire job and finish it off with the finest grade of steel wool.

REFERENCES

A. *Metalwork Essentials*, Tustison and Kranzusch (Bruce Publishing Co.).

B. *Essentials of Metal Working*, Berg and Wing (Manual Arts Press).

C. *Materials of Industry*, Mersereau (McGraw-Hill).

QUESTIONS

1. What is an oxidized finish and how is it applied? (Ref. A, p. 106.)

2. From what parts of the world do manufacturers get the ingredients for tile? (Ref. C, p. 223.)

3. Occasionally we see solder marked "half and half" or "60-40." What does this mean? (Ref. B, p. 122.)

4. With what metal is a tinner's rivet coated? Why? (Ref. A, p. 62.)

5. Why are copper jaws used in a vise?

BICYCLE FLASHLIGHT CLAMP

Safe bicycle operation requires that at night we should have at least a front light. This clamp, designed to fit ⅞-in. diameter handle bars, can be made to fit any diameter flashlight.

MATERIALS REQUIRED

Handle-bar clamp — 1 piece, ⅛ by ¾ by 6½-in. wrought iron.

Flashlight clamp — 1 piece, ¾ by 5⅜-in. 22-ga. sheet iron (small diameter flashlight); ¾ by 6⅜-in. 22-ga. sheet iron (large diameter flashlight).

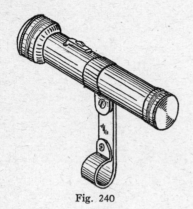

Fig. 240

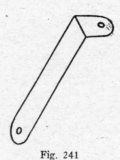

Fig. 241

DIRECTIONS

1. Measure the circumference of the flashlight and add 1¾ in. to the measurement for the flaps. Then make out a bill of material and have the instructor approve it.

2. Cut out the stock as listed in the bill of material.

Handle-Bar Clamp

3. Round the ends on a power grinder and smooth them with a file.

4. Drill a ¼-in. hole, ⅜ in. from each end.

5. Make a right-angle bend 1 in. from the end (Fig. 241).

6. Clamp the piece in a vise over a ⅞-in. round iron bar. Keep the bar near the top of the vise jaws with approximately 1 in. above the top (Fig. 242).

7. Round the piece as far as possible, striking in the direction shown by the arrows in Figure 242.

8. Turn the piece in the vise as shown in Figure 243. The section *B* must be forced down around the bar as far as it will go (note the dotted line).

9. After the part *B* strikes the vise jaw, turn the work in the vise so that the part marked *A* stands back farther in the vise as shown by the dotted circle in Figure 243. Then continue by bending *B* as far back as possible.

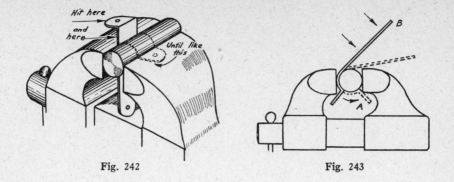

Fig. 242   Fig. 243

10. Finish the bending by placing the clamp in the vise as shown in Figure 244 and bending B back as shown by the dotted line.

11. Where the hole of the clamp meets the back, drill a ¼-in. hole.

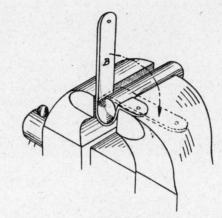

Fig. 244

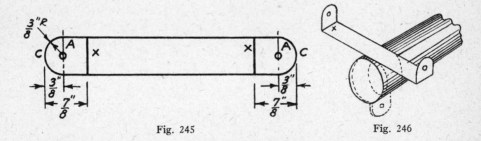

Fig. 245   Fig. 246

Flashlight Clamp

12. Lay out this clamp as shown in Figure 245; first draw lines X, then holes A, and finally curves C.

13. Cut out curves C.

14. Center punch holes A and drill ¼-in. holes (Fig. 245).

15. Make the angle ends at X with a vise and a hammer as shown in Figures 245 and 246.

16. Bend the piece around a stake corresponding to the size of the flashlight (Fig. 246). After it has assumed the round form shown by the dotted circle in Figure 246, slip a bolt through the holes and fasten the flaps together, after which it will be easier to round the piece smoothly.

Assembly

17. Secure the rest of the bolts from the instructor and fasten the clamps together.

18. Clean the clamp with emery cloth and enamel it with the color desired.

REFERENCES

A. *Metalwork Essentials,* Tustison and Kranzusch (Bruce Publishing Co.).

B. *Metal Work,* Jones (Bruce Publishing Co.).

QUESTIONS

1. How long should a piece of metal be cut for a flashlight $1\frac{1}{2}$ in. in diameter, allowing $\frac{3}{4}$ in. for the flaps? (Ref. B, pp. 12, 13.)

2. Why is it important to fasten securely a piece of work for drilling? (Ref. B, pp. 36, 37.)

3. Explain the construction and the use of the circumference rule (Ref. A, p. 2).

4. What are a few factors one must observe in the use of a hack saw? (Ref. A, p. 79).

5. What is drawfiling? When would you use this process? (Ref. A, p. 92.)

DOOR KNOCKER

Many people like to have door knockers on their front door. Here is one of the wrought-iron type, the general design of which may be adapted to any one of the bases shown, or to one of your own design.

MATERIALS REQUIRED

Base — 1 piece, 3 by 6½-in. 18-ga. black sheet iron.
Knocker — 1 piece, ⅛ by ¾ by 7½-in. wrought iron.
Angles — 2 pieces, 1/16 by ½ by 1½-in. wrought iron.

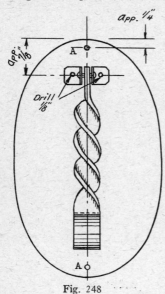

Fig. 248

DIRECTIONS

1. Make out a bill of material and have the instructor approve it.
2. Cut out the stock as listed above.

Base

3. Decide on the shape of the base which should cover an area of 3 by 6½ in. Lay it out on a piece of scrap paper. Use any of the designs shown in Figures 249–252 or make an original one.
4. Have the instructor approve the design and then transfer it to the metal.
5. Cut it out with a tin snips and file the edges smooth.
6. Lay out holes *A*, Figure 248, center punch, and drill them with a 3/16-in. drill.

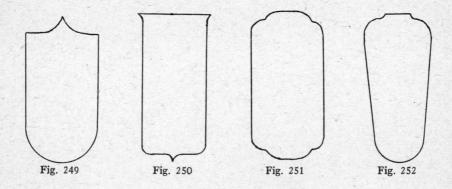

Fig. 249   Fig. 250   Fig. 251   Fig. 252

Angles

7. Grind off the corners 1/16 in. as shown in Figure 253.

8. Lay out the holes and the bending line (Fig. 253).

9. Center punch and drill ⅛-in. holes.

10. Bend the brackets at right angles on the fold line and test them with a square.

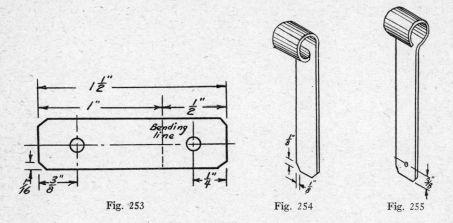

Fig. 253   Fig. 254   Fig. 255

Knocker

11. Grind off all four corners approximately ⅛ in. (Fig. 254).

12. Holding the knocker in the vise, form the round end by bending it around a 1-in. bar with a hammer (Fig. 254 or 255).

13. Lay out the hole, center punch, and drill a ⅛-in. hole (Fig. 255).

14. Twist the piece as desired (see Fig. 256).

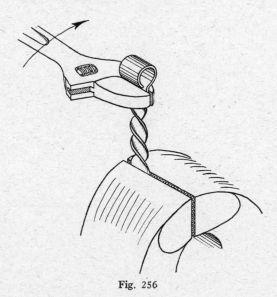

Fig. 256

Assembly

15. Rivet the angles to the knocker, but before doing so insert a small piece of tin plate between one angle and the knocker, which when removed will allow the knocker to turn freely.

16. Hold the knocker assembly on the center line of the base and carefully mark the holes.

17. Drill ⅛-in. holes and rivet the pieces in place.

18. Remove the loose scale from the job.

19. Finish it as desired.

REFERENCES

A. *Metalwork Essentials,* Tustison and Kranzusch (Bruce Publishing Co.).

B. *School and Home Shopwork,* Schultz and Schultz (Allyn and Bacon).

C. *Essentials of Metalworking,* Berg and Wing (Manual Arts Press).

D. *Elementary Wrought Iron,* Bollinger (Bruce Publishing Co.).

QUESTIONS

1. Why is wrought iron so easily shaped? (Ref. B, p. 173.)

2. Name some of the different types of tin snips and give their use (Ref. B, pp. 194, 195).

3. Give briefly the process of making wrought iron (Ref. C, p. 83).

4. What size material can be twisted cold? (Ref. A, p. 114.)

5. What are three ways of laying out metal? (Ref. D, pp. 9, 10.)

STRAIGHT BOOK ENDS

Here is a simple yet effective pair of book ends made from wrought iron. Although the instructions say that the ends should be forged round, there are many other shapes that may be made.

MATERIALS REQUIRED

2 pieces, ⅛ by ½ by 20-in. wrought iron.
4 pieces, ⅛ by ½ in., the lengths to be cut later.

DIRECTIONS

1. Make out a bill of material and have the instructor approve it.
2. Cut the two 20-in. pieces and mark the centers on both.
3. The curve shown in Figure 258 is formed in a bending jig (Fig. 259).

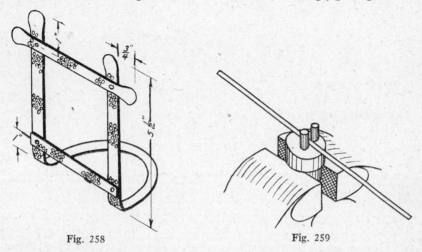

Fig. 258   Fig. 259

4. Bend the ends until they assume the shape shown in Figure 260. The legs must be parallel.
5. The legs will probably be uneven. Use a square to mark them and cut each off so that they will be of the same length.
6. Use a grinder to make the ends round.
7. Heat the ends to red heat and slightly flatten the extremities.
8. Peen the sides with a medium machinists' hammer on a flat anvil (Fig. 258).
9. Lay out the bends, 5½ in. from the top of the legs and bend them at right angles in a vise. Test them for squareness.
10. Lay out the holes shown in Figure 258, 1 in. from the bottom and the top of each leg. Drill ⅛-in. holes.

Bottom Crosspieces

11. Cut two pieces of wrought iron ⅛ by ½ in., the width of the book ends (Fig. 258).

12. File both ends flat and test them with a square.

13. Peen one side as shown in Figure 258.

14. Place it in position over the holes in the legs and scribe the location of the holes.

15. Center punch and drill ⅛-in. holes.

Top Crosspieces

16. Cut two pieces of wrought iron ⅛ by ½ in., 1½ in. longer than the width of the book ends (Fig. 258).

17. Round both ends of each piece on a grinder and flatten them slightly after having heated them to a red heat.

18. Peen one side of each piece.

19. Center them over the holes in the legs and mark the holes with a scriber.

20. Drill the holes with a ⅛-in. drill.

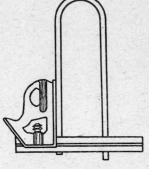

Fig. 260

Assembly

21. Rivet the book ends together with ½ by ⅛-in. roundhead rivets; if necessary cut them off.

22. Clean off the book ends with emery cloth.

23. It is recommended that they be finished with burned oil or dull black enamel.

REFERENCES

A. *Metal Work,* Jones (Bruce Publishing Co.).

B. *Essentials of Metal Working,* Berg and Wing (Manual Arts Press).

QUESTIONS

1. Mention six products made from iron (Ref. A, p. 35).

2. Give the size in decimals of a No. 18 drill, an N drill (Ref. B, p. 154).

3. Explain: hardening, annealing, and tempering (Ref. B, pp. 132–135).

4. Give a safety rule for the operation of gas furnaces.

5. Name three common types of machinists' hammers (Ref. B, p. 57).

CURVED BOOK ENDS

This curved set of book ends not only has an effective design, but also is serviceable as well.

MATERIALS REQUIRED

Base — 4 pieces, ⅛ by ¾ by 3¾-in. wrought iron.
Separators — 2 pieces, ⅛ by ¾ by 3¾-in. wrought iron.
Curve — 2 pieces, ⅛ by ¾ by 13-in. wrought iron.

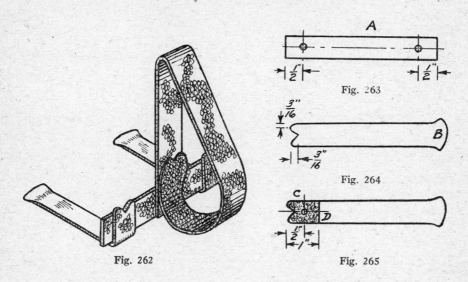

Fig. 263

Fig. 264

Fig. 265

Fig. 262

DIRECTIONS

1. Make out a bill of material and have the instructor approve it.
2. Cut out the materials as listed.

Separators

3. File and test the ends for squareness.
4. Peen one side with a medium machinists' hammer on an anvil (Fig. 262).
5. Lay out holes *A*, Figure 263. Drill them with a ⅛-in. drill and file off the burrs.

Base

6. Hold the end of each piece *B* in a flame until it has reached red heat and flatten it slightly (Fig. 264).
7. Lay out the V shape on the opposite end as shown in Figure 264.
8. Make the V cut with a hack saw and smooth it with a small file (Fig. 264).
9. With the same file round the end as shown in Figures 264 and 265.

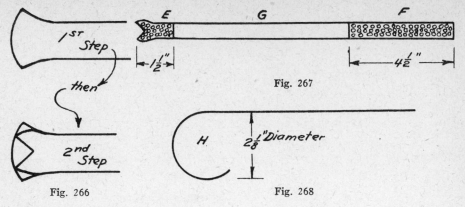

Fig. 267

Fig. 266

Fig. 268

10. Lay out bend *D*, Figure 265.

11. Peen the base piece on one side from the V end to the bend *D* (Fig. 265).

12. Lay out hole *C*, Figure 265, and drill a ⅛-in. hole.

13. Make a right-angle bend along line *D;* test all of the bends with a square.

Curve

14. Square up one end with a file.

15. Form the ornament on the opposite end (Fig. 266). Heat it to a red heat and flatten it with a hammer. Lay out the design with a scriber and cut off most of the waste with a hack saw and finish it with a small file.

16. With a medium machinists' hammer, peen parts *E* and *F* on one side and *G* on the opposite side (Fig. 267).

17. Form curve *H* in Figure 268 by either using a piece of 2⅛-in. round stock or a bending fork. Bend the second piece using the first as a pattern.

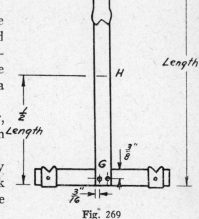

Fig. 269

18. Lay out holes *G* in Figure 269 and drill ⅛-in. holes.

19. Hold the upright piece over the center of the separator (Fig. 269). Make sure that it is square, mark the holes, and drill them with a ⅛-in. drill.

20. Rivet it in position with the round heads of the ⅛-in. rivets on the outside.

21. Lay out bend *H* in Figure 269. This will be the top of the finished book end.

22. Make the bend with a vise and a hammer. The bottom of the curve must rest flat with the base of the book end (Fig. 262).

23. Clean the project with emery cloth, and, if desired, it may be given a coat of lacquer. It may also be given a coat of black enamel. After it has dried, the high spots may be rubbed off with steel wool and then given a coat of lacquer.

REFERENCES

A. *Essentials of Metal Working,* Berg and Wing (Manual Arts Press).
B. *Metal Work,* Jones (Bruce Publishing Co.).

QUESTIONS

1. The lathe is one of the earliest forms of machine tools used by man. Is this statement correct? (Ref. A, p. 138.)

2. What are the three types of taps? (Ref. A, pp. 50, 52.)

3. What precautions must be taken in cutting hard or carbon steel? (Ref. B, p. 16.)

4. Make a simple sketch of a piece of wrought iron, ¾ by 3 in. Show how you would lay out a hole 1¾ in. from one end (Ref. B, p. 29).

5. Give the price of the following tools: 12-in. steel ruler; scriber; tin snips; dividers; blowhorn stake; side cutting pliers (get the price catalogue from the instructor).

CURVED WALL LAMP

This lamp can be fastened to any kind of a wall with two hooks. The simple curves are very pleasing and easy to bend.

MATERIALS REQUIRED

Main curve — 1 piece, ⅛ by ¾ by 24-in. wrought iron.
Small curve — 1 piece, ⅛ by ¾ by 12-in. wrought iron.

DIRECTIONS

1. Make out a bill of material and have the instructor approve it.
2. Cut out the materials as listed above.

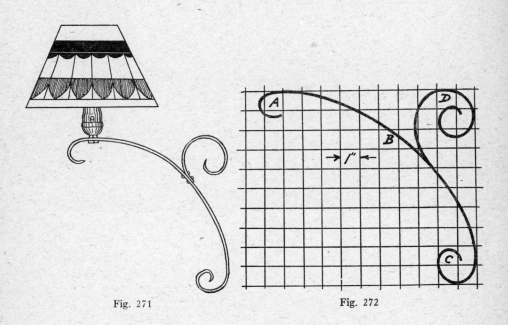

Fig. 271   Fig. 272

Large Curve

3. Decide on the forged ends to be used. Check with the instructor.
4. Forge both ends of each piece on the opposite side.
5. Develop a full-sized pattern from Figure 272.
6. Bend the curves on a bending jig in the following order: curve *A;* gradual curve *B;* and finally curve *C* (Fig. 272). Check the curves continually while they are being bent. Be sure that the forged ends show properly. Another way to form the curves is to make bend *B* first on a slip form roller.
7. Smooth out all the curves so that they flow smoothly into each other without any noticeable bumps.

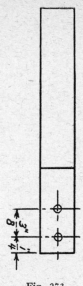

Fig. 273

Fig. 274

Small Curve

8. Forge one end of this piece in the same manner as the large piece. The opposite end should remain square.

9. Form curve *D*, Figure 272, with a jig. Make sure that the forged ends show properly.

Assembly

10. Lay out the holes in the small piece only as shown in Figure 273.

11. Drill the holes with a ⅛-in. drill.

12. Hold the small curve to the large one with a small C clamp. The points *A, B, C,* and *D* in Figure 274 must all touch the square.

13. Mark the points where *A, C,* and *D* touch the square. Also mark the rivet holes.

14. Center punch and drill the holes in the following order: rivet holes, ⅛ in.; holes *C* and *D*, 3/16 in.; and hole *A,* 13/32 in.

15. Rivet the pieces together.

16. Clean the bracket with emery cloth and finish it as desired.

17. Finally wire the lamp with socket, cord, and plug.

REFERENCES

A. *Dictionary of Technical Terms,* Crispin (Bruce Publishing Co.).

B. *Metalwork Essentials,* Tustison and Kranzusch (Bruce Publishing Co.).

QUESTIONS

1. Which is the larger, a 13/32- or a 23/64-in. drill? How much?

2. By a simple drawing, show what you understand by the word *scroll* (Ref. A).

3. With simple sketches, show five different ways to forge wrought-iron ends (Ref. B, p. 98).

4. What safety precautions would you observe in forging wrought iron?

5. What is the main difference between the Bessemer and open-hearth methods of making steel? (Ref. B, pp. 169 and 170.)

ORNAMENTAL SHOE SCRAPER

Besides being effective as a shoe scraper, this project is a bit more ornamental than the simple one described previously. If desired, the design of the scraper blade may be changed to suit one's own taste.

MATERIALS REQUIRED

Blade — 1 piece, 2½ by 6½-in. 18-ga. (or heavier) black sheet iron.
Legs — 2 pieces, ⅛ by ¾ by 11½-in. wrought iron.

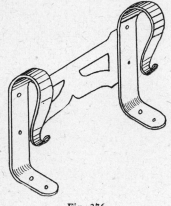
Fig. 276

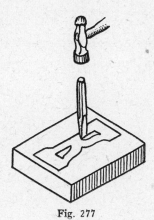
Fig. 277

DIRECTIONS

1. Make out a bill of material and have the instructor approve it.
2. Cut out the material as listed above.

Blade

3. Lay out the blade as shown in Figure 278 or make a design of your own.
4. Cut out the blade with a tin snips, or, if necessary, use a cold chisel.
5. Cut out the interior design of the blade (Fig. 277). Place the metal on a heavy iron block (not an anvil) and roughly chisel out the design. Then smooth the entire outline with files of the correct shape.
6. Lay out holes P, Figure 278. Center punch and make them with a ⅛-in. drill.

Legs

7. The ends of the legs marked X, Figure 279, should be rounded on a power grinder.
8. Lay out the opposite end Y, Figure 279.
9. Cut it out with a hack saw, file the edges smooth, and grind it round as shown.

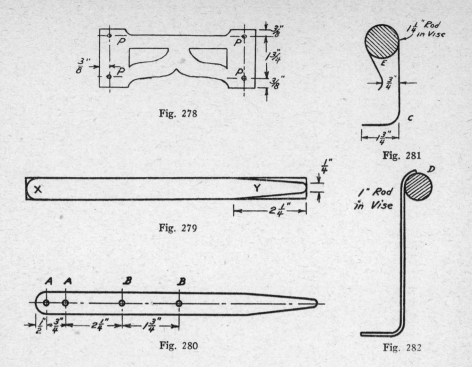

Fig. 278

Fig. 281

Fig. 279

Fig. 282

Fig. 280

10. Lay out holes *A* and *B* shown in Figure 280.

11. Check the locations of holes *B* to be sure that they are accurate by holding the blade over the layout marks.

12. Center punch all the holes. Holes *A* are made with a 3/16-in. drill, and holes *B* with a ⅛-in. drill.

13. Lay out bends *C*, Figure 281.

14. Make the bend at right angles in a vise with a hammer. It ought to be slightly round as shown.

15. Make bend *D*, Figure 282, at the extreme top of the small round end, using a 1-in. round rod, a vise, and a hammer. Bend the two pieces exactly alike and in the right direction.

16. Make bend *E*, Figure 281, over a 1¼-in. bar. It should start just above the holes as shown in Figure 276. A bending fork may be used instead of the bar. Follow Figures 276 and 281 closely. After one leg has been bent to the correct shape, it may be used as a pattern in bending the other.

17. Rivet the legs and blade together with ⅛-in. roundhead rivets.

18. Clean off the scraper with emery cloth and finish it as desired.

REFERENCES

A. *Essentials of Metal Working,* Berg and Wing (Manual Arts Press).

B. *Metal Work,* Jones (Bruce Publishing Co.).

C. *School and Home Shopwork,* Schultz and Schultz (Allyn and Bacon).

QUESTIONS

1. For what are the planing and shaping machines used? (Ref. A, pp. 140, 141.)

2. For what are the flat cold chisel and the cape chisel used? (Ref. A, pp. 33, 34.)

3. Give a safety rule for the use of scribers.

4. What is the difference in the effect of hammering hot iron as compared to hammering cold iron? (Ref. B, p. 24.)

5. How is mild steel manufactured? (Ref. C, p. 174.)

ANCHOR WALL LAMP

Although this lamp has been designed primarily to be used on the wall, it may be readily changed into a table or desk lamp. Additional nautical atmosphere can be added by coiling a small piece of rope around the anchor.

MATERIALS REQUIRED

Disk — 1 piece, 6½ by 6½-in. 22-ga. black sheet iron.
Anchor curve — 1 piece, 3/16 by ¾ by 8-in. wrought iron.
Socket strap — 1 piece, ¾ by 1½-in. 18-ga. black sheet iron.
Anchor upright — 1 piece, ⅜ by ⅜ by 8-in. wrought iron.
Anchor crossbar — 1 piece, 3/16 by 3-in. round cold-rolled steel.

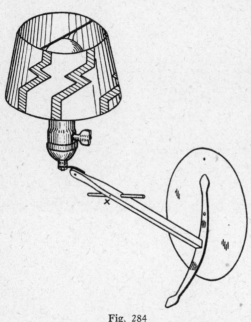

Fig. 284

DIRECTIONS

1. Make out a bill of material and have the instructor approve it.

2. Cut out the materials as listed above.

Disk

3. Draw a 6½-in. circle on the square piece of metal (Fig. 285).

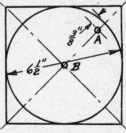

Fig. 285

4. Cut it out with a tin snips and smooth the edges with a file.

5. Lay out holes *A* and *B*, Figure 285. Drill the former with a 3/16-in. and the latter with a ⅛-in. drill.

Anchor Upright

6. Forge one end as shown in Figure 286. Line *Y* is ¾ in. from the end and this portion should be forged to a thickness of ⅛ in. The forging should be gradual as shown at *X* in Figure 286.

7. Grind the forged end round (Fig. 286).

8. Lay out holes *A, B,* and *C* and drill them as follows: tap drill hole *A* for an 8–32 machine screw to at least a depth of ½ in.; make hole *B* 3/16

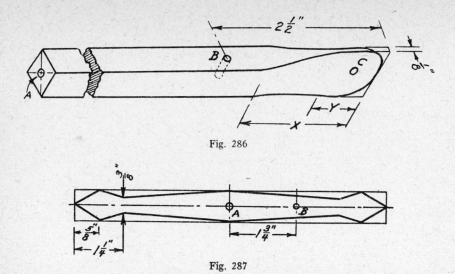

Fig. 286

Fig. 287

in. and be sure that it is on the right side of the piece; finally make hole *C* ⅛ in.

9. Tap hole *A* with a 8–32 tap (see the instructor).

Anchor Crossbar

10. File the ends of the crossbar and check the ends for squareness.

11. Lay out both ends as shown in Figure 287.

12. Make the long cuts with a hack saw, being careful to stay on the line.

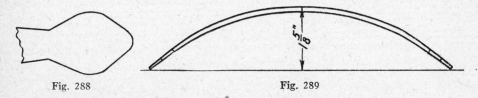

Fig. 288   Fig. 289

13. Round the ends slightly on a grinder as shown in Figure 288.

14. File all of the edges just sawed until they are flat and smooth.

15. Forge both ends back about 1¼ in. so that they are 1/16 in. thick when they are finished.

16. Lay out holes *A* and *B*, Figure 287; drill the former 3/16 in. and the latter ⅛ in.

17. On the extreme left end of the form roller, shape the anchor curve as shown in Figure 289.

Socket Strap

18. Lay out the curved ends of the strap by setting a dividers to one half of the width (Fig. 290).

19. Cut its ends round with a tin snips and file them smooth (Fig. 290).

20. Lay out holes A and B in Figure 290; drill the former with a ⅛-in. drill and punch the latter with a 13/32-in. punch (see the instructor).

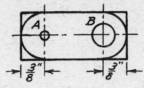

Fig. 290

Assembly

21. Slip the crossbar through the upright and center it in place. With a center punch make an indentation to hold it in place at X, Figure 284.

22. Rivet the socket strap in place.

23. Fasten the upright on the anchor curve with a ½-in. 8–32 roundhead machine screw; be sure to use a lock washer.

24. Rivet the anchor curve to the base.

25. Check the entire lamp to make sure that all parts are in line.

26. Clean it with emery cloth.

27. It is recommended that the lamp be finished with dull black enamel, but any other finish may be used.

28. Make the necessary electrical connections. If the socket is not vertical, bend the strap slightly.

REFERENCES

A. *Materials of Industry,* Mersereau (McGraw-Hill).

B. *Metalwork Essentials,* Tustison and Kranzusch (Bruce Publishing Co.).

QUESTIONS

1. Who were some of the earliest users of iron? (Ref. A, p. 332.)

2. Tell what the invention of the Bessemer process for producing steel did for the steel industry (Ref. A, p. 363).

3. Name five products made from mild steel (Ref. B, p. 158).

4. Illustrate with sketches the difference between single- and a double-cut file (Ref. B, p. 89).

5. What is meant by the feed of a drill? (Ref. B, p. 55.)

BIBLIOGRAPHY

This is a complete list of all the books in the reference sections of each project.

Adams, John D., *Metal Working and Etching* (Chicago: Popular Mechanics Co., 1911).

Berg, Edward and Wing, Bristol S., *Essentials of Metalworking* (Peoria: Manual Arts Press, 1927).

Bergling, J. M., *Art Monograms and Lettering* (Chicago: J. M. Bergling, 1931).

Bollinger, J. W., *Course in Sheet Metal Work* (Milwaukee: Bruce Publishing Co., 1930).

——— *Elementary Wrought Iron* (Milwaukee: Bruce Publishing Co., 1930).

Brady, George W., *Materials Handbook* (New York: McGraw-Hill Book Co., 1937).

Broemel, L., *Sheet Metal Workers Manual* (Chicago: Frederick J. Drake, 1925).

Crispin, Frederick S., *Dictionary of Technical Terms* (Milwaukee: Bruce Publishing Co., 1936).

Dragoo, A. W., and Dragoo, K. L., *General Metal Shop* (Bloomington: McKnight and McKnight, 1936).

Grayshon, Alfred B., *General Metal Work* (New York: D. Van Nostrand Co., 1930).

Griswold, Lester, *Handicraft, Simplified Procedure and Projects* (Colorado Springs: Lester Griswold, 1937).

International Textbook Co., *Chemistry and Materials of Construction* (Scranton: International Textbook Co., 1931 and 1933).

Jones, Harry, A., *Metal Work* (Milwaukee: Bruce Publishing Co., 1933).

——— *Progressive Lessons in Machine Shop Practise* (Milwaukee: Bruce Publishing Co., 1926).

Kronquist, Emil F., *Metalcraft and Jewelery* (Peoria: Manual Arts Press, 1926).

Mersereau, S. F., *Materials of Industry* (New York: McGraw-Hill Book Co., 1931).

Payne, Arthur F., *Art Metal Work* (Peoria: Manual Arts Press, 1929).

Petersen, L. C., *101 Metal-Working Projects* (Milwaukee: Bruce Publishing Co., 1929).

Rose, Augustus F., *Art Metal Work — A Portfolio of Designs* (Providence: Metal Crafts Publishing Co., 1928).

——— *Copper Work* (Providence: Metal Crafts Publishing Co., 1931).

Schultz, Leo C., and Schultz, Louis J., *School and Home Shopwork* (New York: Allyn and Bacon, 1935).

Stanley Rule and Level Plant, *Stanley Tool Chart, C53* (New Britain, Conn.: Educational Department, Stanley Rule and Level Co., 1933).

Trew, Marion S., and Bird, Verne A., *Sheet Metal Work* (Peoria: Manual Arts Press, 1923).

Tustison, F. E., and Kranzusch, Ray F., *Metalwork Essentials* (Milwaukee: Bruce Publishing Co., 1936).

Van Leuven, E. Perry, *Cold Metal Working* (New York: McGraw-Hill Book Co., 1931).

Wakeling, Arthur, *Home Workshop Manual* (New York: Popular Science Publishing Co., 1930).

Willoughby, Geo. A., and Chamberlain, Duane G., *Cold Metalwork Notebook* (Milwaukee: Bruce Publishing Co., 1936).

INDEX